Preface

Zavaleta

M000286445

Title: **Six Sigma and Minitab -** A Complete Toolbox Guide for all Six Sigma Practitioners

Author: Quentin Brook

Publisher: QSB Consulting Ltd
© Copyright QSB Consulting 2006
ISBN Number: 0 - 9546813 - 2 - 0

Published by QSB Consulting Ltd. Contact us or visit our website for more information, volume discounts, online sales and Six Sigma training material licensing.

E-mail: info@QSBC.co.uk
Web: www.QSBC.co.uk
Tel: +44 (0) 7967 754 069

The 1st edition of this guide publication in 2004, and is Sigma practitioners worldw a range of new tools and techniques including new Lean material and Improve tools. In addition it has been updated for Minitab 15 (whilst still compatible with versions 13 and 14).

Cutting through Six Sigma's strange terminology and consultancy speak, this guide delivers Six Sigma in a down to earth, logical and user friendly format.

- **Minitab®:** For each tool, this guide details how to enter the data into Minitab, interpret the results and avoid the common pitfalls.

- **Interactive:** All the data files and templates are available online.

- **Routemaps:** A logical flow is provided through each DMAIC phase.

Who should use this book?

- **Six Sigma Trainees:** Both during and after training, this guide provides an invaluable reference text to those who are actually implementing Lean Six Sigma improvement projects.

- **Six Sigma Project Sponsors and Managers:** For those who are accountable for deploying Six Sigma or sponsoring Six Sigma projects, and who might not have been fully Six Sigma trained, this guide will provide an overview of the tools and techniques that your project teams are trained in.

How To Use This Guide

This guide can be used as an introduction to Six Sigma, a training companion, or a post training reference text.

For each phase of DMAIC - Six Sigma's problem solving approach - this guide provides:

- an overview and route map through the phase
- a checklist for the Six Sigma practitioner
- a list of reviewer's questions for tollgate reviews

Examples: A practical example is provided for each of the tools and techniques discussed. The Minitab data files for these examples can be downloaded online, enabling you to work through the examples yourself in as you read.

The data files can be downloaded from www.QSBC.co.uk

The data file names are indicated on the relevant page, using the symbol:

   "Example File.mpj"

Minitab menu locations are referenced in blue as follows:

Minitab: Stat > Basic Statistics > etc.

NB: The **">"** symbol refers to the next menu level.

The Author

Quentin Brook

Having graduated from the University of Bath (UK) in 1994 with a 1st Class Engineering and Management degree, Quentin developed his experience of statistical quality tools in the automotive industry of Detroit and aerospace industry of the UK.

He trained in Six Sigma with General Electric Aircraft Engines in Cincinnati, USA before becoming Managing Director of QSB Consulting, where he has helped a broad range of clients deploy continuous improvement initiatives in a wide range of industries.

QSB Consulting was formed in 2001, and is a leading provider of Lean Six Sigma training, consultancy, material licensing and project coaching to a diverse range of clients worldwide.

Quentin Brook lives in London, UK.

Acknowledgements

Many thanks to the team of reviewers at British Telecom and elsewhere who user tested this guide and provided invaluable feedback in its development. Thanks also to my family and friends for their support, and particular thanks to:

Kate Adams   Alex Fenton

Vijay Patel   The Minitab team

The QSB Consulting team

Contents

Contents (cont.)

Contents (cont.)

Building a Lean Six Sigma Programme

Using Lean Six Sigma as the backbone of your organisational improvement requires an infrastructure that is focussed on supporting and managing the projects that will deliver the benefit.

Some organisations adopt the entire Lean Six Sigma approach as their improvement programme, whilst others integrate the relevant tools and techniques into their existing programme structure – sometimes without the Six Sigma terminology and "branding". In either case, most improvement programmes will contain the generic components shown above, which are described in more detail on the next page.

Building a Lean Six Sigma Programme (cont.)

Management Awareness and Communication: All improvement initiatives require senior management support combined with an effective communication plan. Successful Six Sigma initiatives can be thought of as a combination of 'pull' and 'push'. Whilst there may be a significant amount of 'push' created by newly trained Green and Black Belts, it is important to create a 'pull' for Six Sigma, led by the senior management. Six Sigma awareness sessions can be useful in demonstrating to senior management their role in generating this 'pull' for data driven decision making – "show me the data!"

Programme Management, Control and Reporting: As the size of a Six Sigma programme increases, a clear management structure is critical for monitoring and reporting on the many projects in progress. This function also includes the tracking of financial benefits accrued by the initiative.

Coaching and Support: The coaching and support provided to newly trained Six Sigma 'practitioners' is the most important factor for driving successful projects forward with pace. Not coincidentally, a lack of coaching and support during their first projects after training is also the most common negative feedback from Black Belts. Support can be provided in a range of formats to cater for the different demands of Green and Black Belts, including:

- Project coaching 'surgeries' to provide detailed one to one support.
- Six Sigma 'helpdesks' (by phone or e-mail) to resolve statistical or Minitab questions that could otherwise cause project delays.
- Six Sigma community events and websites to provide the opportunity for the exchange of ideas and continued learning.
- Guides (such as this one) and training manuals to provide a reference text for referral to after training.

Six Sigma Projects: The value of Six Sigma initiatives is delivered through a broad spectrum of improvement projects. These projects range from small "one Black Belt" projects to larger team efforts, but they all share common features in terms of being clearly scoped, problem orientated and data driven.

The Project Engine: The "project engine" refers to the process of developing a prioritised list of potential Six Sigma projects, that are then taken forward by Black Belt teams. This process starts with a high level analysis of the business, its customers and strategy, in order to develop clear objectives for the Six Sigma programme.

The People Engine: Whilst a large effort is usually devoted to finding the right projects for a Six Sigma programme, far less attention is sometimes paid to finding the right people! Black Belt training is a significant investment and therefore requires careful selection of trainees to ensure that they have the relevant 'change agent' skills.

Training: Six Sigma inevitably involves an amount of training. It is important however to remember that Six Sigma is about delivering real process improvement through structured projects that are *supported* by training where required, not the other way round.

Organisations that focus the majority of their Six Sigma effort solely on training often achieve a large throughput of Green and Black Belts, who then tend to dissolve back into the organisation without generating financial returns through successful projects.

Like all training, *effective* Six Sigma training requires a mixture of theory and practice, based on relevant case studies. Six Sigma trainers should be selected carefully based on their ability to explain and transfer statistics into a range of practical tools, rather than blinding their trainees with complex statistical formulae!

What is Six Sigma?

There are many descriptions of Six Sigma, ranging from a quality level of 3.4 rejects per million, to it being a life changing philosophy!   A more practical definition is *"data driven problem solving"*.

Data driven at every phase: Six Sigma provides a data driven approach to every phase of the problem solving process.

A problem solving structure: Six Sigma provides a structured approach to solving problems. The approach has five phases; Define, Measure, Analyse, Improve and Control (DMAIC).

Data clarity: The Measure phase of Six Sigma ensures that a clear set of measurements are in place to measure process performance *before* the analysis of the problem is started.

Problem focussed: The DMAIC approach focuses on problems, not solutions (therefore projects that have pre-decided solutions are not suitable).

Graphical techniques: Six Sigma reinforces the importance of the basic graphical tools (histograms and run charts etc.) in the analysis of process performance.

A rigorous approach: The DMAIC flow requires discipline. Each step must be completed in order to ensure a project's success in finding and controlling the root cause of a problem... permanently.

Data Driven... ...Problem Solving

Data quality: Despite the ever increasing *volume* of data available, the *quality* of data is often still found to be lacking.   Six Sigma focuses on the quality of data collection, ensuring that process measures are meaningful, accurate and precise.

A generic approach: The DMAIC approach is generic and applicable to **all** environments. Different industries may use specific tools more than others, but the DMAIC phases always remain valid.

A simple approach: The power of the DMAIC problem solving flow lies in its simplicity and clarity. Each phase has clear objectives, actions and outputs.

Statistical techniques : Six Sigma applies the power of statistics in a practical format, enabling users to assess the relevance of statistical results and the risks involved with their decision making.

What is Lean?

A process that is Lean is one that delivers products or services that the customer wants, at a price that reflects only the value that the customer is willing to pay for.

So what does the customer want?

They usually want it immediately!

- so a Lean process must be **fast.**

And they usually want it just how they want it!

- so a Lean process must be **flexible** in order to deliver products and services to the customers exact needs.

And what are they willing to pay for (or not)?

Customers are **not** willing to pay for the costs of:
- making too many products before they are needed
- throwing away or fixing faulty products or services
- delays or unclear communication in the process
- wasted energy during the provision of products and services etc.

These costs are all examples of "waste" in a process, which is a key focus when creating leaner processes - see page 95.

And how do you achieve a Lean process?

In brief, developing a Lean process starts with understanding the value stream of the product or service from the customers perspective.

This can then help you to identify and eliminate waste that the customer will not pay for, and to identify the critical path for products and services to reach the customer quicker.

Recommended further reading:

The lean approach encompasses a massive area of work and techniques, and inevitably far more than we can present in this text as part of Lean Six Sigma.   For more detail on lean, we would strongly recommend texts by J. Womack and D. Jones.

Lean Thinking : Free Press, 7 Jul 2003

Lean Solutions : Simon and Schuster, 3 Oct 2005

The Five Laws of Lean

The Five Laws of Lean encapsulate the Lean approach and provide key principles for improvements.

#1 The Law of the Market effectively says that the customer is king. Critical to Quality characteristics can only be defined by the customer, and should be our highest priority for defining value and making improvements. Everything else, such as sustained market growth and returns on our investments, are reliant on our focus on the customer.

#2 The Law of Flexibility says that the speed and flexibility of a process are linked. An inflexible process will hinder the flow (and therefore speed of delivery) of a product or service, and vice versa for a flexible one. Expanding on this idea further;

▪ If a production line is inflexible (so that it's very difficult to change between products), then this encourages the company to run larger production batches and schedule each product less frequently, both of which will increase Work in Progress (WIP) and lead times of all products.

▪ If a loan company has lots of different types of loan, but it takes its employees a long time to switch between using different forms, processes and IT systems, then again, the employees will be encouraged to batch and queue the loan applications, and it will take longer to get your loan!

#3 The Law of Focus says that 80% of the delays in a process will be caused by just 20% of the activities, and so you should find and focus on these "time traps" in order to create a leaner process.

A similar observation is made when solving quality problems using DMAIC, where you will often find that most of the problems (about 80%) are caused by a few key root causes (about 20%).

#4 The Law of Velocity (a.k.a Little's Law) says that the more WIP there is in a process, the longer its lead time will be. This makes sense, since high WIP means more queues and more waiting between each process step. Little's law can be expressed as an equation, which enables us to calculate the average lead time of a process by knowing how much WIP there is, and the production rate of the overall process – see page 34 for more.

#5 The Law of Complexity and Cost says that products and services that are more complex require significantly more cost to produce and deliver. This may seem in conflict with the first law, in which customers are king and often want highly customised products, but lots of companies are now finding ways to provide "mass customisation" - Dell and Nike are just two well know brands who offer bespoke products.

To summarise, the five laws of lean say that:

#1 Priority should be placed on providing the customers needs.

#2 Processes should be flexible in order to provide products and services faster.

#3 Focusing on key "time traps" will also create significantly faster processes.

#4 Work in Progress (WIP) is a key enemy – since it slows down processes, costs money and hides quality problems.

#5 Unnecessary product complexity should be challenged, but we still need to develop flexible processes that can deliver complex products and services that are customised to individual customers.

Lean and DMAIC

'Lean' provides additional tools and techniques that can be deployed within the DMAIC structure.

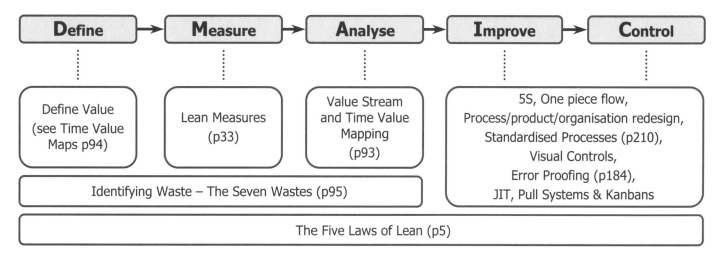

Lean *versus* DMAIC: If you're looking for a discussion of the conflicts between Lean and Six Sigma, then you'll be disappointed, because we don't think there are any!

The two approaches contain a complimentary range of tools and techniques. In reality, most projects, will inevitably require a range of both Lean and Six Sigma techniques.

DMAIC is a very effective problem solving structure that helps you to be clear about what you are trying to achieve. For that reason, we would recommend utilising Lean techniques as and when they are needed within a DMAIC structure, as shown above.

More lean tools: This text focuses on Six Sigma combined with an overview of the Lean approach and a selection of its key tools (above).

There are a large number of Lean tools that can be deployed within the Improve and Control phases, and we have inevitably not been able to provide details on all of them.

Different types of Lean Six Sigma projects

Lean Six Sigma provides a generic approach to problem solving, but its application will involve a wide spectrum of projects, from smaller local improvements through to larger more advanced projects.

Lean Six Sigma projects:

There is no clear distinction between Lean and Six Sigma when it comes to real life projects. You might hear people saying they are working on a "lean project" or a "DFSS project" (Design for Six Sigma), but in reality they are all trying to improve processes and products.

Instead, every projects tends to be unique in terms of the tools that are found to be useful, and the diagram below demonstrates the two extremes of the spectrum.

It's not all about size!

Local improvement projects are not necessarily smaller projects (but they do tend to be). Some local projects have produced significant savings when rolled out across an organisation.

A more important aspect of a project is the **type** of problem involved and the most appropriate tools for solving it.

The following page shows the different types of tools and techniques that might be applied for local improvement projects versus those that are useful in advanced projects.

Local improvement projects.

The Lean Six Sigma project spectrum...

From leaner projects.... ...to the more Six Sigma orientated

Advanced improvement projects

- Many, rapid incremental improvements
- A 'Just Do It' type approach
- Smaller teams
- Local scope
- Lower projects savings (but not always!)
- Local deployment and locally led
- Practical, cheaper solutions

- Fewer, more substantial, step change improvements
- In-depth analysis, requiring longer timeframes
- Larger teams with senior sponsorship
- Broader scope, often part of larger initiative
- Higher project savings or strategically critical
- Local **and** company wide deployment
- Mixture of practical **and** sophisticated solutions

Different types of Lean Six Sigma projects (cont.)

Local improvement projects		Advanced improvement projects
Loose framework, with strong focus on Improve	**DMAIC Framework**	Rigorously applied with strong focus on D, M & A to ensure successful Improve and Control
Rarely required for local improvement projects	**Advanced Statistical Tools**	GR&R, Capability Analysis, DOE, Regression, Hypothesis testing, Process Modelling
Basic Process Mapping, Cause and Effect, 5 whys, Paretos, Time Series Plots, Histograms etc.	**Quality and Graphical Tools**	Basic techniques plus advanced tools such as QFD, KPI trees, Run charts, Scatter plots, Multi-Vari analysis, FMEA etc.
Basic lean techniques – Value Stream Mapping, Time Value Mapping, Seven Wastes etc.	**Lean Tools**	Basic Lean tools plus advanced application of lean principles, one piece flow, complexity, JIT etc.
Small project teams led by process owners, therefore requiring less engagement skills	**Project and Team Management Skills**	Strong leadership and stakeholder management skills are critical to success of larger projects

Managing Lean Six Sigma Projects

Like all projects, Lean Six Sigma projects require effective project management to succeed.

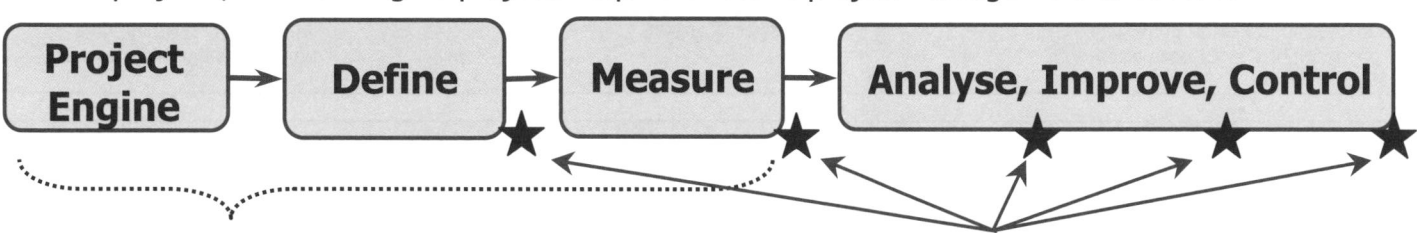

The screening process:

The 'project engine' (described on page 2) is a screening process that takes a broad range of project ideas and reduces them down to a prioritised list of potential Six Sigma projects.   However the screening process doesn't stop there.   Project reviews at the end of the Define and Measure phases should also be considered as 'screening' points, at which Six Sigma projects can be held or stopped if the conditions are not right for them to continue. The ability to stop projects that no longer have the right components for success is an important characteristic of a 'mature' Six Sigma programme.

Why might projects get stopped?

Projects can be held or stopped at the Define phase review for a variety of reasons including lack of sponsorship, lack of resource, unclear problem and goal statements, an unclear business case, low potential returns, etc.

Although less likely, projects can also occasionally be stopped at the end of the Measure phase if, for example, the problem has been found to lie in the way the process is being measured rather than its actual performance.

Project Reviews/Milestones/Tollgates:

Good project management involves the development of clear project plans that include milestones and associated deliverables. It makes sense to align the project plan milestones with the DMAIC phases of Six Sigma, as shown above. A checklist and review questions are provided at the end of each DMAIC phase throughout this text.

Project Documentation:

The most effective method of documenting a Six Sigma project is the use of a project working file that is updated (as a presentation) as the project progresses. Like a presentation, the project working file provides a summary of the project to date, which can then be used as the basis of project coaching and reviews.

The DMAIC phases of the project should be clearly demonstrated throughout the project file.

The value of maintaining a working file is that it promotes project clarity by encouraging a Black Belt to continuously summarise their progress within the DMAIC structure.

Minitab – Overview

What is Minitab?

Minitab is a statistical software package that is commonly used by Six Sigma analysts. Minitab is not the only software that contains the tools of Six Sigma (many of the functions can be recreated in spreadsheets such as Excel with a little programming), but it has become the market 'standard' for Six Sigma use. For more information on Minitab, visit:

www.minitab.com

Minitab Menus: All the menu commands quoted in this text are based on the standard menus of Minitab 15 (with version 13 and 14 differences noted where applicable).

QSB's Customised Minitab Menu: Versions 14 and 15 allow the customisation of the menu structure, so that you can group together your favourite Six Sigma tools into a single menu. These customised menus and settings can then be saved as a 'profile' and shared with other users of Minitab.

All of the tools and techniques discussed in this guide have been grouped together into a single Minitab menu, which is available as a profile for download online at:

www.QSBC.co.uk

The profile (called QSBC Customised Minitab Menu) is explained in more detail in Appendix C, along with detailed installation instructions and a menu map. The profile can be easily switched off or removed from your version of Minitab if no longer required.

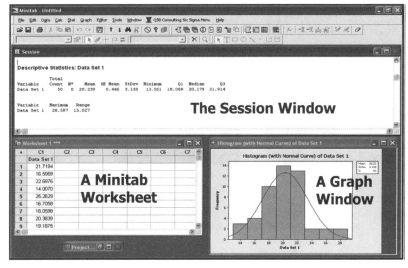

The picture above shows a typical image of the Minitab software. A Minitab 'project' file always contains several standard types of 'window', as follows:

The Session Window: Minitab files always include a session window that contains all the numerical analysis results conducted to date for that file.

Worksheet Windows: Data is entered and stored in worksheet windows which are similar to spreadsheets. See the next page for notes on entering data into Minitab.

Graph Windows: Each graph output is placed in its own window, as shown by the histogram example above.

Minitab – Data Types and Data Manipulation

We are used to arranging data in spreadsheets in a way that is easily readable to the human eye. A feature of Minitab however, is that it **always** requires data to be stored in columns.

	Jan	Feb	Mar	Apr
Location 1	289	295	300	301
Location 2	70	73	75	76
Location 3	168	174	180	189

A typical spreadsheet file may look like this (left);

But in Minitab the same data must be arranged like this:

The raw data in the spreadsheet above – the numbers, the locations and the months – must all be given their own columns in Minitab. This is because many of the functions in Minitab work on a whole column of data at once.

Minitab also assumes that data in the same row is linked, so the data can be arranged in several different ways (including the two alternatives shown on the right) as long as the rows still correspond with each other.

Different types of data in Minitab: Minitab recognises three types of data – numeric, text, and dates. It does this automatically, and adds a 'T' (text) or a 'D' (date) to the column number if required.

or

Worksheet 1 *

	C1 Data	C2 Location	C3-D Month
1	289	1	Jan
2	70	2	Jan
3	168	3	Jan
4	295	1	Feb
5	73	2	Feb
6	174	3	Feb
7	300	1	Mar
8	75	2	Mar
9	180	3	Mar
10	301	1	Apr
11	76	2	Apr
12	189	3	Apr

Worksheet 1 *

	C1 Data	C2 Location	C3-D Month
1	289	1	Jan
2	295	1	Feb
3	300	1	Mar
4	301	1	Apr
5	70	2	Jan
6	73	2	Feb
7	75	2	Mar
8	76	2	Apr
9	168	3	Jan
10	174	3	Feb
11	180	3	Mar
12	189	3	Apr

❗ Be careful when cutting and pasting data into Minitab. If there is just one bit of text in a column of numeric data, it will recognise the whole column as text. If this happens, delete the text, and convert the column back to numeric, using:

Minitab: ***Manip > Change Data Type (Version 13)***
Minitab: ***Data > Change Data Type (Versions 14 & 15)***

❗ Missing data is shown as an asterisk (*) in Minitab. These are inserted automatically if required.

Minitab – Graphs

The first steps of data analysis are always graphical techniques. Minitab offers a wide range of graphs and provides suggestions as to the most appropriate one for the analysis tool you are using.

For correlations

For plotting distributions

For comparing groups of data

For analysing categories of data

For studying trends over time

For 3D graphs

How to find graphs in Minitab: Minitab provides access to graphs in two ways.

- The *Graph* menu (left) offers a range of common graphs.

- Alternatively, when you are using a statistical function, Minitab usually offers a number of graphs that are appropriate to the analysis you are doing.

Graph Management: You'll soon find that Minitab gets very full with numerous graphs.   The key is to remain in control, which can be done by being disciplined about:

- (re) naming your graphs – so the title reflects what the graph is showing.
- close down any unwanted graphs, and minimise those you want to keep.
- save graphs you want to keep for a long time as a separate file (ext: "mgf").

Graph Discipline: Don't forget the basics when you create a graph. Make sure that each graph has a **title**, axis **labels**, a note of the **sample size** and a record of the **units** used.

Minitab – Graphs (cont.)

Minitab 14 and 15 offer a significant step forward in the quality and features of the graphs available.

Updating graphs with new data:

Unlike Excel, if you create a graph in Minitab it will not necessarily be updated if you then subsequently change the original data. In version 13, you will need to create the graph again, but versions 14 and 15 provide the ability to update graphs.

The status of a graph is indicated by the (small) symbol in the top left corner of the graph window, as follows:

▪ A green cross (on any background) means that the graph is up to date, and still reflects the original data that it was based upon.

▪ A yellow symbol means that the graph is **not** up to date, but **can** be updated.

▪ A white cross means that the graph is **not** up to date, and **cannot** be updated (this can happen for a variety of reasons – you will have to create the graph again).

How do you update a graph?

1) Right click the graph, and select **Update Graph Now** or **Update Graph Automatically**, or

2) Go to *Minitab: Window > Update All Graphs Now*

Customising a graph: Most aspects of a graph can be customised and amended after you have created the graph, by double clicking on the feature you are interested in.

Additional features (such as reference lines, subtitles, distribution fits) can be added by going to: *Minitab: Editor > Add*

Minitab – Graphs (cont.)

Dotplot of Parcel Weight (Kgs)

Parcel Weight (Kgs)

Graph 'Brushing': Minitab has a 'brush' tool that allows a graph to be 'interrogated' in order to identify which row number a specific data point comes from.

The mouse is used to click on specific groups of data (indicated by the dashed line square in this example) and the relevant row numbers appear in a small brushing window.

At the same time, a black dot is placed by each relevant row number in the associated worksheet, for easy reference.

Minitab: Editor > Brush

Row	Location	Business Type
6	France	Residential
7	England	Residential
9	France	Residential
12	France	Commercial
18	England	Residential
26	France	Residential
29	England	Residential
32	England	Commercial
36	England	Residential
46	France	Residential
47	France	Residential
53	France	Commercial
54	England	Commercial
56	France	Residential
73	France	Commercial

Brushing

Advanced Graph 'Brushing' Techniques:

1) Setting ID Variables:

In addition to showing the row numbers of the brushed area on the graph, the Brushing window can also be used to show information from other columns in the worksheet. In this example, the Location and Business Type of the brushed dots are also being shown in the brushing window, alongside the row numbers.

This is done using *Minitab: Editor > Set ID Variables*

2) Creating an Indicator Variable:

Minitab can also create a column of data that is based upon the data points that have been brushed on the graph. The default output is that brushed points will be recorded as **1**, and others as **0**.

This is done using *Minitab: Editor > Create Indicator Variable*

DMAIC – A Logical Flow To Problem Solving

The 'DMAIC' problem solving approach is simple and logical. Understanding and adhering to its simplistic nature is the key to a successful Lean Six Sigma project.

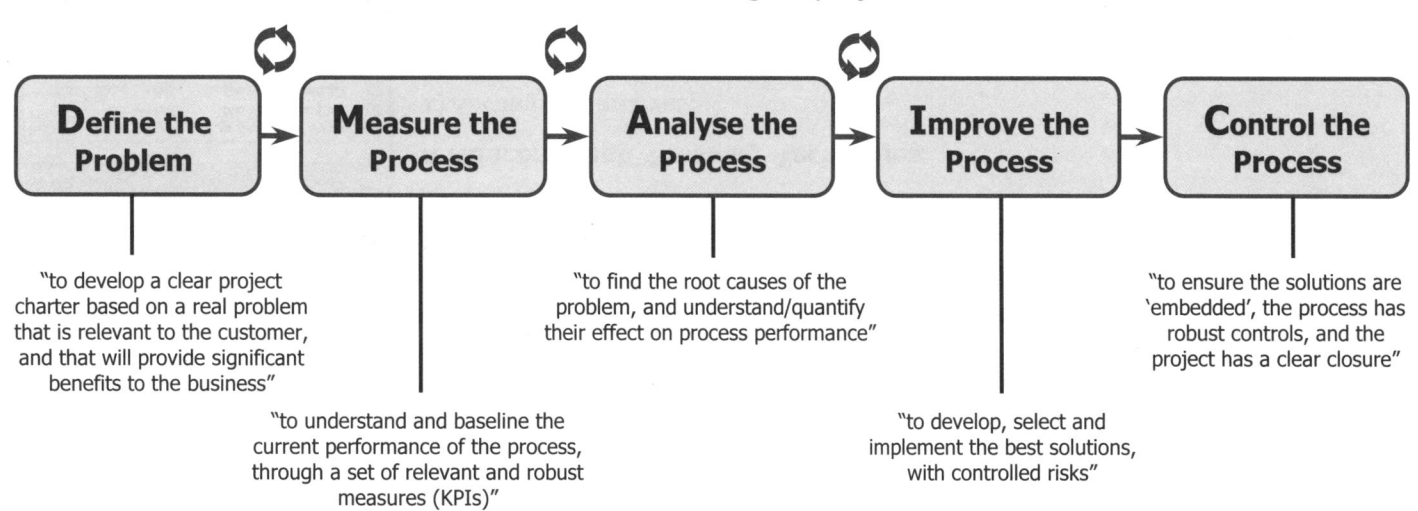

Define the Problem → **Measure the Process** → **Analyse the Process** → **Improve the Process** → **Control the Process**

"to develop a clear project charter based on a real problem that is relevant to the customer, and that will provide significant benefits to the business"

"to understand and baseline the current performance of the process, through a set of relevant and robust measures (KPIs)"

"to find the root causes of the problem, and understand/quantify their effect on process performance"

"to develop, select and implement the best solutions, with controlled risks"

"to ensure the solutions are 'embedded', the process has robust controls, and the project has a clear closure"

Gain Project Approval: The end of the Define phase is a decision point. A project review is required to assess the Define phase outputs, to gain a consensus that the project is worth doing, and to commit the resources required for it to succeed.

An iterative approach: Despite the rigid nature of the DMAIC flow, the first four phases (Define through to Improve) are often iterative in their application.

Close the Project: Successful projects need clear and visible closure, the key elements of which should include; documenting lessons learnt, 'transfer' of the process back to 'business as usual', and finally, celebrating success!

Overview of Define

The DMAIC process starts when you have identified a problem. The Define phase helps to clarify your understanding of **why** it is a problem, before investing time and money in the project.

The flow through Define:

Define the Business Case	Understand the Customer	Define the Process	Manage the Project	Gain Project Approval
What's wrong? And what do you want to achieve?	How does the problem link to the customer?	Are you clear which process the problem relates to?	Who? Where? When? How?	Does the project have the buy-in to proceed and succeed?

THE TOOLS AND TECHNIQUES FOR DEFINE

Problem Statements (p17) Goal Statements (p19) Costs of Poor Quality (p20)	Voice of the Customer (p21) Kano Analysis (p22) Critical to Quality (CTQ) Trees (p23)	SIPOC Process Map (p24)	Project Structure (p25) Project Plan (p25) Stakeholder Analysis (p26) Project Working Files (p27)	Project Charter (p28)

Six Sigma projects start with problems, not solutions: The Define phase focuses only on the problem – root causes and solutions come later on. If the project already appears to have a proposed solution, or the project title infers one, it is the Project Leaders role to turn the project around to being "problem - orientated".

Problem Statements

A problem statement is a simple but powerful tool that is not as easy as it looks!

Problem statements are a brief but specific description of the problem. They should clearly explain what the problem is, how often it occurs, and what the impact is (cost) when it does occur.

What makes a good Problem Statement?
- **Keep it brief** – two or three short sentences at the most.
- **Avoid technical language** – you should be able to explain the problem in simple terms.
- **Quantify the problem** – use any data you have available.
- **Explain the cost of the problem** – you should refer to the key "costs of poor quality" (p20) of the problem.
- **Define the scope** – use terminology that helps to define the scope of the project.

Use the **SMART** checklist below to challenge how good your statement is. Is the problem statement:

Specific?

Measurable?

Achievable? (Goal statement)

Relevant?

Time Bound?

Some Problem Statement examples:

1) During 2006, 20% of overseas customer payments took longer than the agreed invoice terms. This resulted in an average outstanding debt of £357K, at a 5% cost of capital.

2) From Oct 05 to March 06, 5% of Product A manufactured on production line 1 failed the final test. This resulted in an extra inspection/rework process being implemented (at a cost of £25,000 per month), and a scrap rate of 2% costing £20K/mth in lost revenue.

What is good about these examples?
- Both of them provide dates and data that help 'baseline' the problem.
- The scope of the problems are defined by phrases such as *product A, overseas* & *production line 1*.
- Both statements explain how the problem affects the organisation and provide an estimate of the cost.
- They do not refer to any solutions or root causes.

Problem Statements – How Low Should We Go?

A common difficulty in developing problem statements is deciding how detailed to make them and at what process level they should be pitched within the organisation.

The answer is to make sure your problem statement **does not** define a problem to which you **know** the answer.

Starting at the top...

"The business is not making enough profit!"

This is clearly too broad for a Six Sigma project – you cannot solve all the problems at once.

In addition it is not "SMART" enough to be a problem statement (see page above).

And! – realistically you probably know why the business is not making enough profit.

So, try the next level down...

"During the last 12 months, our operating costs have been approx. 20% above the best in class/target, leading to reduced profits."

This is getting more manageable – it's focusing on a lower level output within the business (operating expenditure) rather than a high level output (profit).

But, it is still a little too widely scoped for a Six Sigma project.

So, try the next level down again...

Rework levels within the billing process of the Southern area office have been running at 70% for the last 12 months. This drives increased operating costs (labour, IT, office space), lost revenue and low customer satisfaction.

Finally, this problem statement appears to be at an appropriate level for a Six Sigma project.

It's clearly scoped, it's "**SMART**", and it focuses on a problem to which the root cause is not yet known (why are rework levels so high?)

It also goes on to explain how the problem costs the business money.

Goal Statements

The goal statement responds to the problem statement and defines the target for the project.

Goal statements should be as brief and specific as the problem statements to which they respond.

What makes a good Goal Statement?
- Keep it brief.
- Avoid technical language.
- Use the same metrics as the Problem Statement.
- Be as specific as possible about dates.
- Avoid defining the solution to the problem.

How do you set a Goal during the Define phase?
At this point in the project, it's obviously difficult to quantify how much the process will be improved by. There are a couple of options available:

- State your best estimate at this stage - to be revised later.

- Use an "X" (as in example 2 opposite) – which means you will fill it in as soon as you can estimate it.

The Goal statement is typically reviewed at the end of the Measure and Analyse phases to ensure it remains realistic.

Some Goal Statement examples:

1) Reduce the percentage of overseas customer payments that take longer than the agreed invoice terms from 20% to 5%, by the end of quarter 4, 2007.

2) Reduce the Product A final test failure rate on production line 1 from 5% to X% by the end of October 2006.

What's good about these examples?
- Both of them set a date for the improvement to be achieved by.
- Both of them are specific about the process measurement that will be improved.
- Neither of them contain a solution or root cause.
- They define success as improvement in a key measurement.
- They are brief.

Costs of Poor Quality (COPQ)

The Six Sigma phrase 'Cost of Poor Quality' refers to all the costs associated with the problem.

There are many Costs of Poor Quality (COPQs) that are recognised easily, such as rework, rejects, inspection, testing, customer returns and complaints etc. However behind these, there is usually a large range of COPQs that have become so common that we start to view them as 'normal', such as excess inventory, late payments, expediting costs, high employee turnover etc.

COPQ and the Problem Statement

The problem statement should contain the **main** category of COPQ that impacts the business financially. For example, the financial impact of the problem may be lost revenue, material scrap costs, the labour costs of rework or the cost of capital tied up in excess inventory etc.

However, there are usually many different COPQs for each problem, and it is worth expanding on these aside from the problem statement.

Hard versus Soft Benefits

Hard versus Soft Benefits: When a problem is solved, the COPQs help define a range of hard and soft benefits that will be created. This terminology is used to describe whether the benefit can be measured financially (hard) or non-financially (soft). Whilst a project's business case will be based on the hard benefits, the softer benefits such as "improved customer satisfaction" should not be ignored, as it may be possible to convert them to hard benefits eventually.

It is important to involve the finance department in a review of a project's benefits during the Define phase, in order to agree how an improvement in process performance will be converted into financial savings at the end of the project.

Different types of 'Cost of Poor Quality'

It may be useful to use the following categories for thinking about costs of poor quality. However, it is only a framework to help ensure you don't miss anything in your COPQ assessment.

Appraisal: This refers to any systems, processes or procedures that exist only to look for problems, such as inspection. How often do you do something and then immediately check it?

Prevention: There are also lots of systems and procedures to prevent things going wrong. Whilst beneficial they are still actually costs of poor quality.

Internal Failure: Problems that occur 'within' the business may not impact the customer directly but they should still be seen as costs of poor quality. Eventually these COPQs will reach the customer in the form of higher prices or delays.

External Failure: An external COPQ is the cost of any defect that reaches the customer. These costs of failure can become very significant.

Voice Of The Customer (VOC)

Even the smallest Six Sigma project must take the time to ensure it is customer focussed. On a practical level this involves **talking** to and **becoming** a customer in order to understand their needs.

Different methods of researching the VOC:

- **Customer complaints** – a good place to start but be wary about possible bias.

- **Direct contact methods** – phone calls, focus groups, interviews at the point of provision.

- **Less direct methods** – surveys, feedback cards, market research and competitor analysis etc.

- **Becoming a customer** – phone your own call centre, order groceries from your own on-line store, buy one of your own brand washing machines, set up a new account with your own bank etc.

There is no excuse not to consider the VOC!

Most Six Sigma projects are too small to have a budget for formal customer research, and they don't usually need it. The internet has huge quantities of market research made public by various organisations and many of the methods and suggestions on this page require nothing but time.

No project is too small to do VOC.

Some practical examples of collecting the VOC:
(Remember to think practical – VOC research cannot be done from the office, you have to get up and go and meet the customer!)

Example 1: For a project that aims to reduce the cost of collecting insurance premiums from residential customers, select a few random customers and ring them up and talk to them about the reasons behind their choice of payment method (credit card/direct debit/cheque/cash etc.)

Example 2: For a project that aims to improve customer satisfaction of a home delivery service, go out with a delivery van for a day or two and talk to the customers directly at the point of delivery. What features are important? How would they prioritise them? What is acceptable? What is not acceptable?

Example 3: For a project focusing on the production quality of an aeroplane component, go and talk to the customer's engineers and understand the thinking that went into their design of the component, its tolerances and materials etc.

Kano Analysis

Customers provide all sorts of feedback when collecting the VOC. The Kano model is a framework for categorising and prioritising the different performance features of a product or service.

The Kano model identifies three categories of performance features of a product or service:

'*Must haves*' fulfil a **basic requirement** of the customer and the customer assumes they will be present. You do not get any extra points for providing these features, but the customer will notice if they are missing, so they are known as **dissatisfiers**.

Examples of **must have** features of a modern car are a reliable engine and a radio.

'*More is betters*' fulfil a **performance requirement.** The more you provide of these features, the more the customer is satisfied, so they are also known as **satisfiers**.

Examples of **more is better** features of a modern car are the efficiency of the engine, the range of the vehicle between refuelling and (for some people) the number of cup holders!

'*Delighters*' fulfil an **excitement requirement**. These are the features of a product or service that provide a 'wow' factor, and really delight the customer – hence their name!

The problem with identifying **delighters** is that even the customer won't necessarily be able to express what features would delight them, because they haven't experienced them yet!

Examples of **delighter** features of a new car might be having the car delivered right to your front door a week earlier than estimated, with a free bottle of champagne on the front seat.

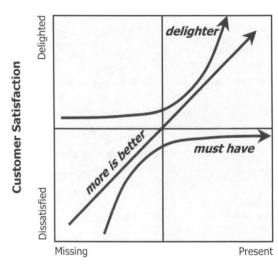

Required or actual feature of the product or service

Different ways of using the Kano model...

▪ You can map existing or proposed features of your products & services into the Kano categories, to better understand how your product or service fits customer needs.

▪ You can ask customers to do the same, in order to better understand the VOC.

▪ You can use the Kano model to categorise and structure general customer feedback.

❗ The Kano model often highlights how customer requirements are constantly changing. Today's **delighters** become tomorrow's **must haves**, requiring us to constantly develop new, differentiated customer offerings.

Critical To Quality (CTQ) Trees

Having gained an insight into the Voice of the Customer, it can be useful to present the results in a tree format. This provides clarity and a structure for developing quantifiable specifications.

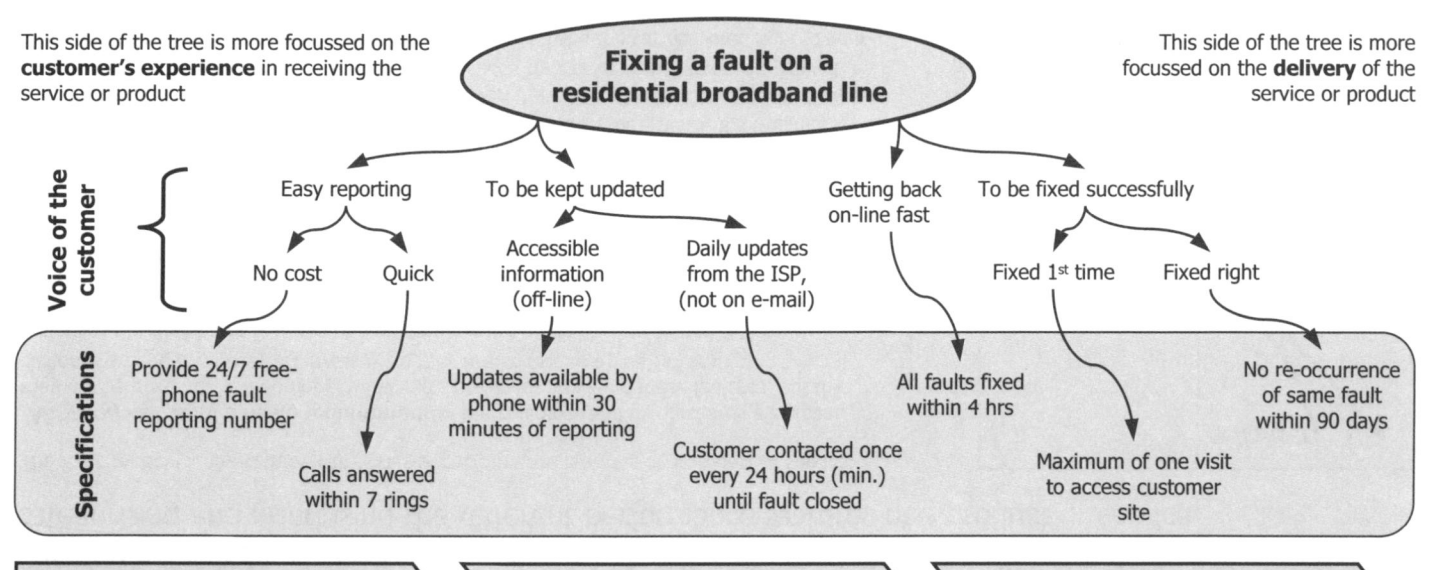

This side of the tree is more focussed on the **customer's experience** in receiving the service or product

This side of the tree is more focussed on the **delivery** of the service or product

Fixing a fault on a residential broadband line

Voice of the customer

Easy reporting

To be kept updated

Getting back on-line fast

To be fixed successfully

No cost

Quick

Accessible information (off-line)

Daily updates from the ISP, (not on e-mail)

Fixed 1st time

Fixed right

Specifications

Provide 24/7 free-phone fault reporting number

Calls answered within 7 rings

Updates available by phone within 30 minutes of reporting

Customer contacted once every 24 hours (min.) until fault closed

All faults fixed within 4 hrs

Maximum of one visit to access customer site

No re-occurrence of same fault within 90 days

The aim of a CTQ tree is to provide clarity around the aspects of the VOC; in this case getting the fault fixed quickly, effectively, and with maximum ease and information.

The categories are then broken down into more specific requirements, such as 'no cost', 'accessible information off-line' etc.

Finally, each requirement is translated into a specific 'measurable' characteristic that is 'Critical to (the) Quality' of the process of fixing a residential broadband fault.

SIPOC – High Level Process Mapping

It is too early for **detailed** process mapping – that comes in the analyse phase.   But a simple process definition and map at this stage can help ensure everyone understands the core process.

SIPOC stands for Supplier, Input, Process, Output and Customer.

What does the SIPOC do? SIPOC is a tool for clarifying the core process that a project is focused on.   This can then be used in the Define phase review in order to check that all the stakeholders of the project agree on the core process involved.

The SIPOC Process:

1) A SIPOC starts with a simple definition of the process

2) The 4-6 key steps of the process are then expanded at the bottom of the SIPOC

3) The main inputs and outputs of the process are then listed.

4) The suppliers of each input and customers of each output are then identified.

Suppliers	Inputs	Process	Outputs	Customers
Operations	Product delivery date		Invoice	Client
Sales	Client data	**Issue an invoice**	Due date	Accounts receivable
Accounts	Payment terms		Sales data	Sales
Legal	VAT Rules		VAT data	Accounting

Check client terms → Write invoice → Print invoice → Address and send invoice → Record data with sales

"SIPOC Template.ppt"

Project Structure and Project Plans

As with any other project, a Six Sigma project needs a project team with a clear structure, roles and responsibilities, together with a preliminary project plan.

A Typical Project Structure will include:

- A **Six Sigma Champion** – the project should have the support and awareness of the relevant Six Sigma Champion, whose role is to ensure that the project fits within the bigger picture of the Six Sigma strategy.

- The **Project Sponsor -** who is responsible for the project. Be warned! – too many Project Sponsors will see their role as an adviser, with no responsibility for the success of the project.

- The **Project Leader** – usually a Black Belt, who leads the project on a day to day (and preferably full time) basis.

- **Team members** – often trained to Green Belt level and involved part time.

Who to involve in your team:

- Ensure all the relevant processes are represented in the team that you select.
- Pick the right people – don't just end up with those available!
- Do not recruit too many people – you can always call in additional support at the right time. 4-6 is about right.

Project Planning:

At the Define stage, it will only be possible to assign approximate dates for your project, but this is still important in order to communicate your expected rate of progress.

Milestone /Tollgate reviews are an essential part of a project, ensuring there are clear deliverables at every stage.
The key points of a successful review are:
- The whole project team should be involved (before and during).
- Ensure the stakeholders are present (Champion / Sponsor etc.)
- Provide a summary to date, with key findings.
- Prepare, and allow time, for questions.
- Ensure any support requirements are made clear.
- Present clear next steps.

Checklists and Review Questions for each DMAIC phase.

It makes sense to structure project milestones around the DMAIC phases and so at the end of each phase, this book provides:

- a **Checklist** to help the project team develop milestone deliverables.
- a list of **Review Questions** for use by the stakeholders attending the review.

Stakeholder Analysis

Stakeholder analysis is something we do naturally every day without realising it. A structured approach provides a clear strategy for managing the stakeholders effectively and appropriately.

What is Stakeholder Analysis?   Stakeholder analysis is the process of considering those people that will be involved or affected by the project, or who have some level of control over the project and process.

Different formats for Stakeholder Analysis: There are several formats for conducting an analysis, but they all tend to focus on two criteria (as shown in the stakeholder mapping tool opposite):

▪ **Power** – the role of a stakeholder and their relationship to the project determines their **ability** to support the project, or to hinder its progress.

▪ **Position** – the position of a stakeholder as a Blocker or Supporter and their level of interest will determine their response to a project.

Communication Plans:

Stakeholder analysis is not something you just 'do' and then file away.   Its purpose is to help create a strategy for the day to day management of key stakeholders, in order to minimise the potential project blockers. This strategy is often termed a **communication plan** but in reality its scope also covers the more subtle aspects of how a stakeholder should be involved in the project. A communication plan doesn't need to be a very formal affair, but for each key stakeholder it should detail:

- ▪ the **format** that will be used to communicate with the stakeholder (e.g. e-mails, 1-2-1's, invite to team meetings/reviews, weekly informal chats etc.)
- ▪ who is going to be the **primary contact** responsible for managing key stakeholders
- ▪ **key actions** for each stakeholder – an action plan to influence specific key stakeholders.

Project Working Files (Storyboards)

The most effective method of documenting an improvement project is through the use of a project working file that is written as a presentation, kept updated as the project progresses, and structured clearly around the DMAIC phases.

The value of maintaining a working file is that it promotes project clarity by encouraging a project leader to continuously summarise their progress within the DMAIC structure.

There are several additional advantages to maintaining an ongoing working file, including:

- The file can be used as the basis of project coaching sessions.
- Preparation time for tollgates (reviews) is minimised.
- Preparation of final project reports is quicker, with more detail available.
- Projects are reported in a consistent, recognisable format – a typical group of core slides for Define, Measure and Analyse are shown below.

Define: Problem and Goal Statements
Costs of Poor Quality
CTQ Tree
SIPOC Map
Project Plan
Project Charter

Measure: KPI Tree
Operation Definitions
Data Collection Plan
Measurement System Analysis
KPI 1 – Process Capability
KPI 2 – Process Capability

Analyse: Detailed Process Map
Value Stream Map or Time Value Map
FMEA
Brainstorming & Fishbone Diagram
Graphical analysis
Statistical analysis
Etc...

Project Charter

A project charter is used to summarise the findings of the Define phase of the project.

The importance of 'pace' in the Define phase: Too many projects take too long to complete the Define stage, causing a lack of momentum before the project even gets started! In practice, the Define phase should be viewed as a screening process. The process generates a clear project scope, business case and project team, but it should also be possible for a project to be stopped at the Define phase review – the potential benefits might not be sufficient, the availability of resource might be an issue, or the solution may be pre-prescribed. A rapid pace through Define indicates that the project has the support and resource it needs to succeed.

Where does the Project Charter fit in?

To help the Define phase review, a Project Charter (also known as a summary/mandate/project description) is a **one page** document that enables all the stakeholders to review the project and commit to its support. A Project Charter is the Six Sigma equivalent of the more traditional formal project approval processes.

A typical Project Charter contains:

- **Project Title –** this should state what the project is going to do.
- **Team Structure** – Project Sponsor, Project Leader, Team Members.
- **Problem Statement** and **Goal Statements.**
- **COPQ** – a summary of the cost of the problem to the business.
- **VOC** – the key customers and their Critical to Quality issues (CTQs).
- **Scope** – the scope of the project in terms of products, departments, locations, processes etc.
- **Stakeholders** – the key stakeholders.
- **Project Plan** – planned dates for completion of the DMAIC phases.

Project Charter

Project Title:	

Project Team		Stakeholders	
Role	Name	Role	Name
Project Sponsor		Six Sigma Champion?	
Project Leader			
Team Members			

Problem Statement	Goal Statement

COPQ Summary	VOC - key customers

Scope	Project Plan	Plan	Actual
	Start of project		
	End of Define		
	End of Measure		
	End of Analyse		
	End of Improve		
	End of Control/Project		

 "Project Charter Template.xls"

Define – Checklist

- ❑ Is the problem clear? And is there data/evidence to support the problem statement?
- ❑ Are the goals of the project clear (Goal Statement) and are they realistic at this stage?
- ❑ Does the project have a clear business case? (a problem linked to Costs of Poor Quality linked to business benefits)
- ❑ Has the potential business benefit been estimated in cash?
- ❑ Is the process involved clearly understood? (using SIPOC?)
- ❑ Are the customer(s) of the process clear? (Both internal and external)
- ❑ Are the customer's needs understood? And supported by evidence/data?
- ❑ Is the project focused on a customer requirement?
- ❑ Is the scope of the project clear?
- ❑ Are the key stakeholders in the project/process identified and a communication plan in place to manage them?

Project Management

- ❑ Does the project have clear sponsorship?
- ❑ Is there a team in place with the time and resources to complete the project (within current scope)?
- ❑ Is there a structure in place for managing the team on a short term basis?
- ❑ Is a preliminary project plan in place (including planned finish date)? Does the plan have clear milestones and deliverables?

Define – Review Questions

- Why this project?
- How does it relate to the businesses needs? (strategic/operational)
- In what ways does the problem impact the bottom line (cash)?
- How much of the problem do you hope to eliminate?
- Does the team have first hand experience of the process? If not, how do they intend to get it?
- How does this project relate to the end customer? Who is it?
- What has been done to **really** understand the customers requirements (VOC)?
- What is the scope of the project? Are there any issues or overlaps with other projects to resolve?
- Has this problem been looked at before?... What happened?
- Who are the key stakeholders in the project? Why?
- How will the stakeholders be managed?

Project Management

- Who is accountable for this project's success? (The Sponsor?)
- Is the project team in place? If so, who was selected? Why?
- Does the project have enough time/resource?
- Have the key team members freed up their time for this project?
- How will the team be managed?
- How will the project be documented?
- What are the key milestones within the project plan?
- What are the next steps right after this review?

Overview Of Measure

The Measure phase aims to set a stake in the ground in terms of process performance (a baseline) through the development of clear and meaningful measurement systems.

The flow through Measure:

Develop process measures	Collect process data	Check the data quality	Understand process behaviour	Baseline process capability and potential
How do you measure the problem?	When and where does the data come from?	Does the data represent what you think it does?	How does the process currently behave?	What is the current performance of the process with respect to the customer?

THE TOOLS AND TECHNIQUES FOR MEASURE

KPIs (p31)	Data Collection Methods (p46)	MSA (p53)	Distributions (p67)	Process Capability (p74)
Lean Measures (p33)	Data Collection Plans (p47)	Resolution (p56)	Normal Distribution (p69)	Capability Analysis (p76)
Statistics (p35)	Sampling (p47)	Continuous GR&R (p58)	1st Pass Analysis (p71)	Cp (p81), DPMO (p82)
Operational Definitions (p37)	Contextual Data (p52)	Attribute GR&R (p61)	Process Stability (p72)	Sigma Levels (p85)
Data Worlds (p40)		MSA Drilldown (p66)	Short/Long Term Variation (p73)	Sigma Shift (p87)

! Don't be tempted to jump ahead to root causes (Analyse) or solutions (Improve) until the process can be measured effectively. The Measure phase builds upon the existing data available (introducing new data collection and measurements if necessary) in order to fully understand the historical 'behaviour' of the process. Team members on their first Six Sigma project often find the Measure phase surprisingly detailed and rigorous but with experience, realise that it is a worthwhile investment that always pays off later in the project.

Key Performance Indicators (KPIs)

Having understood your customers CTQ features, they are then used as the basis for your KPIs.

What are Key Performance Indicators (KPIs)? KPIs are measurements that reflect the performance of the process. The terminology "KPI" is widespread but they can also be called primary metrics. KPIs need to reflect the Voice of the Customer, and so the example below builds upon the Critical to Quality characteristics developed in the broadband repair example on page 23.

"CTQs" (from page 23)	Calls answered within 7 rings	Updates available by phone within 30 minutes of reporting	All faults fixed within 4 hrs	Maximum of one visit to access the customer site	No re-occurrence of same fault within 90 days
Customer driven KPIs	% calls answered within 7 rings	% updates available within 30 mins	% of faults fixed within 4 hours	% faults fixed with one (or less) visit to access customer site	% of faults with no re-occurrence within 90 days
The data you will need to collect	Time to answer each call	Time between fault reporting and update being available	Time to fix each fault	Number of visits to access customer site	Number of re-occurrences of fault within 90 days

Collecting the right data for KPIs:

Customer driven KPIs are usually percentages that classify the process output into pass or fail categories based upon the customer's CTQs.

However, in order to calculate these KPIs, you should aim to collect the 'raw' data of the process (such as the actual time to answer each call).

Efficiency versus Effectiveness:

The KPIs shown here focus on measuring the **effectiveness** of the process in the eyes of the customer. However, a project should also have some KPIs that reflect the **efficiency** of the process from the business perspective. Efficiency KPIs are included in the KPI tree (next page).

Key Performance Indicator (KPI) Trees

A KPI Tree is a visual method of displaying a range of process measures that are relevant to your project or process. It's particularly useful for demonstrating the different categories of measures.

Fault Repair Project KPI Tree

Fixing the fault	Interacting with the customer	Managing the business
% fixed within 4 hrs		**Average resource hours per fault**

Fixing the fault:
- **% fixed within 4 hrs**
  - % faults fixed in one or less visits
    - Average # of visits / fault
  - % faults with no re-occurrence within 90 days

Interacting with the customer:
- % customers satisfied with repair service
- **Helpdesk**
  - % calls answered within 7 rings
    - Average answer time
  - % updates available within 30 minutes

Managing the business:
- **Average resource hours per fault**
  - # faults repaired per week
  - # repair department employees

Logical categories

It is useful to structure your KPI tree into logical categories, and to then check that you have found the right mix of KPIs to represent each section.

KPI Trees are a tool for bringing together a range of measures that are relevant to the situation (either a project or a process). Often, these measures will already exist within the organisation, and you can therefore 'source' them from other KPI trees. Alternatively, you might find that sometimes you have to develop some new measures.

A balanced approach: A successful KPI tree is one that contains a balance of measures covering both the **efficiency** and **effectiveness** of a process. So, for the example above where the project might be focused on improving the **speed** of repairing faults, the KPI tree also contains measures of customer satisfaction and the resource costs of repairing them. This is because it would be crazy to improve the speed of repair, only to find that your 'improvements' have made the customers more unhappy and that you have doubled the costs of repairing a fault!

So, you need a balance of measures covering quality, delivery and cost.

Lean Measures

There are a number of Lean Measures that can be used to assess the "lean performance" of a process.

VA = Value Add
Non-VA = Non Value Add

Processing Time (PT) = The lead time of an individual process step

Queue Time (QT) = The queuing time between two process steps

Total Value Add Time = The total processing time of the Value Add processes (excluding step 2 in this example)

Work in Process (WIP) = The number of products or services waiting between steps, or being processed within a step

Total Lead Time = The total time for a product or service to pass through the whole process from start to finish

Complete rate = The number of "things" that are completed in a specific time period (e.g. a minute, hour or day etc.)

Takt Time = The average customer demand rate. So a Takt Time of 6 minutes indicates that on average a customer demands a product or service every 6 minutes

Lean Measures (cont.)

The Lean Measures can be combined to calculate a range of Lean KPIs, as follows:

Process Cycle Efficiency (PCE) is the primary lean measure, combining elements of both speed (lead time) and value.

It represents the proportion of time spent in the process that a product or service is actually being worked on in a way that is adding value for the customer.

$$PCE (\%) = \frac{\text{Total Value Add Time}}{\text{Total Lead Time}}$$

So what PCE does a Lean process have?

As always, it depends on the type of process and environment, but here are some guidelines...

▪ Typical transactional and service type process have a PCE of up to 10%, and a world class lean target would be 50% or more.

▪ Typical production processes have a PCE of up to 20%, and a world class lean target would be 25%, or more for continuous processes.

Benchmarking PCE is difficult due to the different ways in which Value Add Time can be measured. However, the most important issue is that **you** measure it in a consistent way, and improve on it.

Lead Time (the speed of a process) is an important Lean KPI. It can be calculated directly by measuring actual lead times from the process, or alternatively an average lead time can be calculated using Little's Law below.

This method is a useful reminder that WIP is a major cause of long lead times, and that reducing WIP is one of the best ways of achieving a faster process.

$$\text{Average Lead Time} = \frac{\text{WIP}}{\text{Completion Rate}}$$

Takt Time (the drumbeat of a process): is also an important lean measure, but it is not strictly a KPI.

Instead, it represents the rate of customer demand and is calculated by dividing the available work time in a day, by the number of products required by the customer in a day. Being aware of the Takt time is critical when designing a lean process, in order that it provides products at the rate the customers require them.

$$\text{Takt Time} = \frac{\text{Available Work Time}}{\text{Customer demand}}$$

Statistics for Summarising Process 'Position'

It is more than likely that your chosen KPIs involve an 'average' of some kind. Despite the common use of the average, it is worth remembering that there are alternatives!...

Alternative terminology for the average:

- **Mean** – sometimes used instead of average.

- **$\overline{X}$** – (pronounced 'X Bar') – used to represent the average of a sample.

- **µ** – (pronounced 'mu') – used to represent the average of the total population.

Note - In theory X Bar and Mu are for use in different situations. Whilst academics may get worried about this, Six Sigma is about practical statistics and they tend to be used interchangeably.

The two features of a histogram are its central **Position** and **Spread**:

The **Spread** of the histogram (how wide it is) is important because it gives an indication of the amount of variation in the process. This is explained further on the page below.

The **Position** of the histogram refers to where the process is centred.

There are two common statistics that can be used to reflect Position:

1) The Average – commonly used because it is easy to understand and calculate. The average works well where the process is reasonable symmetrical and there are not any 'outliers' (unexpectedly small or large data points) which can significantly affect the calculation of the average.

2) The Median – less widely used, but a useful statistic due to its 'robustness'. The median is defined as the middle value of the data (the 50th percentile) and its calculation is not significantly affected by any outliers in the data.

Where Average and Median are different:
This example of a 'skewed' distribution shows the differences that can occur between the average and median. The average is pulled to the right by the high value outliers. Which statistic to use is down to the situation and the pros and cons discussed above.

Statistics for Summarising Process 'Spread'

Six Sigma focuses on reducing process variation and so a measurement for variation is essential.

Standard Deviation = 10
Range = 60

The **Spread** of the histogram indicates the amount of variation in the process. There are two alternative statistics that can be used to measure variation:

1) Range – commonly used because it is easy to understand. The range is the difference between the maximum and minimum results, and because of this 'simple' approach it is not very robust. Just one outlier in the process will increase the range dramatically.

2) Standard Deviation – is a more robust measure of variation, but it is perceived as difficult to understand because it is not easy to picture what it is. See below for an explanation.

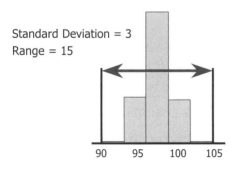

Standard Deviation = 3
Range = 15

What is Standard Deviation?
A practical definition of Standard Deviation is:
"the average distance of the data points from their own average".

The distance of the data points from their own average is shown graphically here by the dotted lines on the Time Series plot. ➡

The symbol used for standard deviation is the Greek symbol ' **σ** ' - pronounced Sigma!

Average

💾 **"Distributions.mpj"** contains a selection of the different distributions shown over the last two pages.

Operational Definitions

Operational Definitions are developed to provide clear and unambiguous descriptions of each KPI.

Components of an Operational Definition

- **KPI Name:** The terminology selected must be used consistently throughout the project. It is also useful to number the KPIs (for the duration of the project at least).

- **What is the KPI supposed to represent:** A 'down to earth' description of the measurement, that someone not involved in the company or project could understand.

- **Process Diagram or Drawing:** (see next page)

- **Detailed definition:** Providing more detail aims to avoid any areas of ambiguity that might lead to the measurement being recorded differently by different people or systems.

- **Measurement Scope:**
Although this is largely defined by the scope of your project, it might be that the scope of some measurements cannot be entirely coordinated with the scope of your project.

What happens without an Operational Definition:
- Unreliable data will be collected in different ways
- Different standards will be applied in different areas

An Operation Definition example for the Fault Repair Time KPI (referenced on pages 31 and 32):

KPI Name: Fault Repair Time

What does the KPI represent: The time elapsed between the customer reporting the fault and the service provider informing the customer the fault is fixed.

Process Diagram — see next page.

Detailed Definition:
Process start – the time (in day/hr/min/sec) that the fault handling centre logs the call or e-mail as 'received'.
Process stop – the time that the phone call or e-mail (informing the customer the fault is fixed) is made/sent at.

Customer Focussed KPIs: At this point, it is often found that existing measurements are not very customer focussed.   For example, the fault repair time (above) is measured from the time at which the fault is reported, but would clearly be more 'customer focussed' if measured from the actual time of failure.

In reality this is usually more difficult to measure, and so a compromise is required.   The benefit of developing an Operational Definition is that the project team are forced to consider these issues, where they might otherwise have been ignored.

Operational Definition Diagrams

A process diagram or picture is an essential part of an effective Operational Definition.

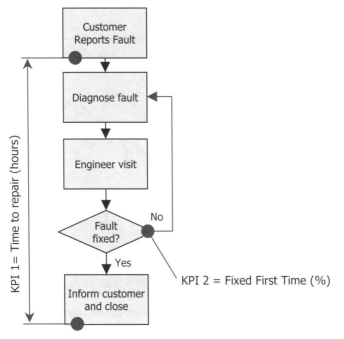

Example 1: A simplified process map can be used to demonstrate which parts of the process the KPI refers to. Numbering the KPIs provides a consistent reference for the rest of the project.

KPI 1: **Time to repair (hours)**

The diagram indicates that the time to repair starts at the end of the fault reporting process and stops after the customer has been informed and the fault 'closed'.

KPI 2: **Fixed First Time (%)**

The diagram indicates that the 'Fixed First Time' measure represents the percentage of faults that **are** fixed after the engineer's visit (regardless of the reason).

! Units: Always specify the measurement units in an Operational Definition

Operational Definition Diagrams (cont.)

Example 2: The measurement (and units) of the width of this ring pull are indicated on a photograph.

Example 3: The acceptability of a defect on this weld is best demonstrated in a photo (or with a real sample part).

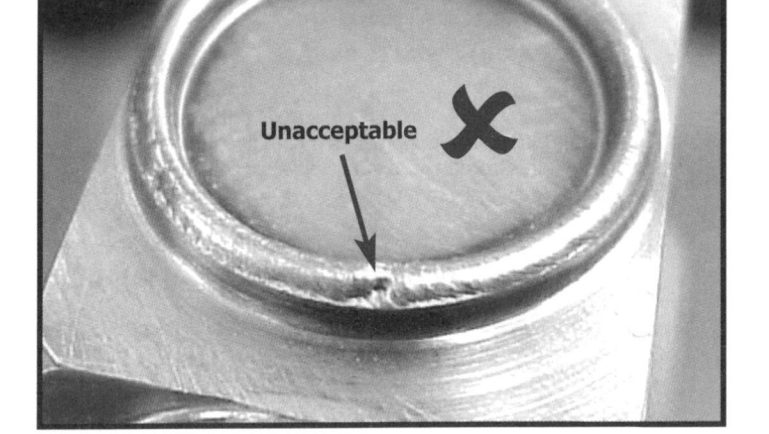

Data Worlds – Overview

All numeric data can be placed into one of the three Six Sigma 'data worlds' described below. Understanding the different data worlds is an important discipline of Six Sigma because it has implications for the type of analysis, tools and techniques that will be used later on.

The Six Sigma data world is likely to be...	The **"Continuous"** data world (p41)	The **"Count"** data world (p42)	The **"Attribute"** data world (p43)
When you are...	**'Measuring'** something	**'Counting'** things	**'Classifying'** something
The clues to look out for are...	If you have calculated averages and variation, and if the resolution of your data is only limited by how good your measurement system is.	If you are counting whole things, or if the data can only be integers.	If you are categorising things into different categories that do not necessarily have any numerical value or order (e.g. pass/fail).

Data Worlds – a forgotten principle: Many training programs do not cover data worlds in enough detail. Understanding the different data worlds and their implications in detail is critical to ensuring that a Six Sigma analyst will be able to select the right tool or technique when back in their work place.

❗ There are a variety of different terminologies used for the data worlds which can be very confusing. Appendix D compares and explains the different terminologies in more detail. The terms **Continuous**, **Count** and **Attribute** will be used consistently throughout this guide.

The 'Continuous' Data World

55.8
56.4
36.2
59.7
54.8
54.0
43.3
42.9
53.7
31.2
63.8
45.3
34.5
44.3

Continuous data results from **measuring** a product or service characteristic.

This data (left) is typical of Continuous data because it is clearly not limited to whole numbers.

This data could represent:
- time to fill new job vacancies (days)
- the diameter of a metal shaft (mm)
- oven temperatures (degrees)
- letter weights (grams)
- pressure (kg/cm2)
- invoice processing time (days)

Note: Always state the units of Continuous data

! **A trap to avoid with Continuous data:** Sometimes the resolution of the measurement system can affect how the data appears.

For example, data on the processing times of invoices might be rounded to the nearest day (so the data opposite would be 56, 56, 36, etc.). This is still Continuous data, but it can be misleading because the measurement system may only record whole numbers, making the data look 'discrete'.

A histogram – a common tool for analysing Continuous data:

A statistical model that Continuous data sometimes follows (under certain conditions) is the Normal distribution (see page 69 for more details).

A graphical tool often used for analysing Continuous data is the histogram, as shown on the right.

Statistics: Continuous data is usually summarised by statistics such as *average* and *median* (which indicate the position of the data), and *range* and *standard deviation* (which indicate how wide the distribution is).

The 'Count' Data World

As the name implies, Count data results from **counting** things.
Sometimes you will be counting defects and sometimes counting volumes.

These data sets (left) are typical of **Count** data because they are all whole numbers. This data could represent:

- errors on invoices
- applicants for vacant job positions
- calls to an IT helpdesk during each hour
- scrap parts in each production batch
- scratches on sheets of glass
- parcels delivered in a day

A **histogram** is often used for analysing Count data (see right).

The statistical model that Count data follows (when under statistical control) is the Poisson distribution, which is shown on the histogram opposite. The distribution is skewed to the right, because it is impossible to count less than zero.

Statistics: Count data is usually summarised by calculating the **average** results. This is commonly known as the average "Defects per unit" (DPU), and for the examples above might be 'average errors per invoice' or 'average number of applicants per job vacancy' etc.

How to spot Count data:

- **Half units are not possible –** half an error, half an applicant, half a call, or half a scratch just don't happen!
- There is **no physical upper limit –** in theory there is no upper limit to any of these Counts.
- Count data is always recorded for a **specific area of opportunity** such as an invoice, a vacant position or an hour of IT helpdesk time.

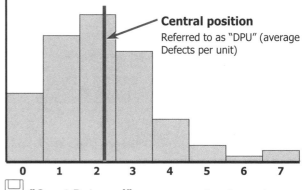

Central position
Referred to as "DPU" (average Defects per unit)

"Count Data.mpj" contains examples of several different ways in which Count data can be recorded in Minitab.

The 'Attribute' Data World

Good			
Bad	Pass		
Good	Fail		
Good	Fail	On time	
Bad	Pass	Not on time	1
Good	Pass	On time	0
Good	Pass	On time	1
Good	Pass	On time	0
	Pass	Not on time	1
	Pass	On time	1
		On time	1
			1

Attribute data results from **classifying** things.

All the data sets on the left are typical of Attribute data in its 'raw' state. The first thing you notice is that they are not all numerical data, but there are always only two categories, so Attribute data tends to look binary, as in the example containing '0's & '1's.

Depending on the industry sector involved, these data sets could represent:
- computer inspection results
- network availability
- part availability
- on-time delivery
- helpdesk problem resolution
- customer satisfaction

"Attribute"	Sample Size	%
2	8	25.0
3	10	30.0
10	90	11.1
8	65	12.3
5	40	12.5
4	41	9.8
30	252	11.9

Raw and Summarised Data:

The table on the left contains Attribute data in a **summarised** format. Each line represents a 'sample' of **'raw'** Attribute data.

So, the first line (2 out of 8) **summarises** the same information shown in the **raw** data samples from the top left of the page.

The third column is the same Attribute data converted into percentages.

The statistical model that Attribute data follows (when under statistical control) is the Binomial distribution. Everyday examples that follow the Binomial distribution include tossing a coin, picking a playing card, or throwing a dice.

Statistics: Attribute data is usually summarised as percentages. Percentages are one of the most common statistics in use, and in every case, a percentage implies that there were two categories of possible results, such as pass/fail.

"Attribute Data.mpj" contains examples of several different ways in which Attribute data can be recorded in Minitab.

Comparing the Data Worlds

The performance of most processes is reported as a percentage (Attribute data). However, the Continuous and Count data worlds have more resolution and are therefore more valuable for analysis.

The graphs opposite show how Continuous or Count data can always be summarised as Attribute data.

The **performance** of a process is usually reported in % (Attribute data), because it is simpler to understand.

However, **analysis** of the problem is far easier in the 'richer' data worlds of Continuous and Count data.

Of course, it is also a compromise of:

▪ **Cost:** Continuous and Count data 'cost' more because they take longer to collect and require more complex collection systems. It is far easier and quicker to implement an Attribute data system that just categorises results into groups of Pass or Fail.

▪ **Resolution and Understanding:** Continuous and Count data provides more resolution. Instead of classifying a product or service into one of two categories (pass or fail), they provide more understanding of the extent to which something was good or bad.

So....

Instead of asking the customer if they are satisfied or not (Attribute) – try and grade the satisfaction between 1 and 10 (Continuous).
Instead of recording if the delivery was on time or not (Attribute) – try and measure exactly how late it was (Continuous).
Instead of asking if the car was clean or not (Attribute) – count the number of bits of dirt that were still there (Count).
Instead of recording if the diameter of the football was within official specification (Attribute) – measure how big it was (Continuous).

Statistics and Data Worlds – Summary

Building on the overview slide at the beginning of this Data Worlds section (p40), this summary incorporates the relevant statistical models and statistics that have now been introduced.

	Continuous	**Count**	**Attribute**
If the Six Sigma data world is...			
Then a relevant statistical model is...	The **Normal** distribution	The **Poisson** distribution	The **Binomial** distribution
When the statistical model applies...	Not all the time – the validity of the Normal model needs to be checked	The Poisson model always applies if the process is "in-control"	The Binomial model always applies if the process is "in-control"
Common statistics are...	Average (mean), Standard Deviation (sigma)	Defects per Unit (DPU)	Percentage (Proportion)
Useful graphs	Histogram (p104) Time Series Plot (p109)	Histogram (p104) Time Series Plot (p109)	Time Series Plot (p109) 100% Stacked Bar Chart (p121) Pareto Chart (p112)

Data Collection Methods

Data collection is an expensive process and yet most companies collect large amounts of data with high duplication. Successful data collection is driven by clear goals and a focus on preparation.

Existing or new data collection?   Be careful not to assume that the existing data will be suitable for your project. Instead, use the Operational Definitions to decide if existing data sources can be used.

Two key types of data collection:

1) In-Process – where data collection is integrated into the process and therefore recorded automatically.

2) Manual – where the data collection system is additional to the process and recorded by text or typing.

Checksheets are **manual** data collection forms which enable the information to be recorded by 'checking' the pro-forma sheet in the appropriate space.   They are generally used to collect information on a temporary basis (i.e. for the duration of a Six Sigma project).

- **Traveller Checksheets** – stay with the product or service throughout the process, collecting information at each stage.
- **Failure Checksheets** – collect information on the reasons for failure at specific process steps (see example on this page).
- **Visual Checksheets** – use pictures of the process or product to record where a failure occurred (e.g: car hire damage diagrams).

Invoice Number	Supplier	Reason for Failure				
		No PO	Wrong Value	Carriage not agreed	VAT wrong	Other
454	Pro-Form	✓				
A633	Magna-Tech			✓		
A657	Magna-Tech					Not received
LKS22	LKS	✓				
LKS25	LKS				✓	
	Pro-Form			✓		

Hints and Tips for Checksheets:

- Design the checksheet with a team of people who are going to use it.
- Keep it clear, easy and obvious to use – and trial it first.
- Communicate – if you don't let people know why they are being asked to fill in a checksheet, then they won't fill it in!
- Traceability – do not forget to record names, dates, serial numbers. This is useful contextual data – see page 52.
- Beware the 'other' column – if you end up with all your failures being classed under this column, then your reasons columns are not the right ones.

Data Collection Plans and Sampling

Having decided what to measure and how to record it, a Data Collection Plan specifies how much data will be collected (the sample size), and how often (the frequency).

Measure 100% or take a sample?

Too many organisations measure 100% of their output. This *"if in doubt - measure it"* approach is driven by a lack of confidence in the statistics.

In reality, most of the value of collected data is gained from the first few measurements taken – known as the "minimum sample size" – and collecting more data than necessary provides ever decreasing returns in (statistical) confidence.

Data collection from a Population or Process?

1) Collecting data from a static group is focused on a **Population**. Every day examples include: taking a water sample from a swimming pool to estimate its chlorine content or market research with a focus group to estimate the populations view. In this situation the main data collection decision is what **sample size** to use (how much data to collect).

2) Collecting data on an ongoing basis in order to detect changes over time is focussed on a **Process.** Everyday examples include: tracking the fuel consumption of a car over its lifetime or monitoring a commute time to work.   In this situation the data collection decision is not only what **sample size** to use (how much), but the **sampling frequency** as well (how often).

"Sample Size" (how much data) – (next page) is based on the following considerations:

- The type of data (world) involved

- The existing variation in the process

- The precision required of the results

"Sampling Frequency" (how often) – (p51) is based on the following factors:

- Any natural cycles that occur in the process

- The precision required of the recorded data

- The volume of products or service produced

Minimum Sample Sizes – Continuous Data

The most common question concerning data collection is "how much data should we collect?" Unfortunately the answer is often "it depends". But! – there are some *minimum* guidelines as follows:

For Continuous Data, calculate the minimum sample size as follows:

The Process

↓

Estimate the standard deviation of the process (see opposite).

↓

Decide on the precision that you require

↓

Calculate the minimum sample size (MSS) as follows:

$$((2 * \text{standard deviation}) / \text{Precision})^2$$

NB: If the minimum sample size exceeds the parts available, measure them all (100%)

Example: Collecting data to assess the lead time of an invoice process. (Units are days)

↓

Historically invoices have taken anywhere from 10 – 30 days. So say standard deviation = 4 days

↓

Required precision = +/- 2 days

↓

$$\text{MSS} = ((2 * 4) / 2)^2$$
$$= 16$$

So to estimate the mean invoice lead time to with +/- 2 days, you should collect at least 16 pieces of data.

Estimating standard deviation

Knowing the variation in the process (standard deviation) helps to achieve a more realistic sample size. But how do you estimate standard deviation when you haven't even measured the process yet? The answer is that you estimate it.

A very basic approach for estimating standard deviation is to look at the historical range of the process (the difference between the highest and lower results that you've seen) and to divide it by 5.

Normally, there are 6 standard deviations in the range, so this is a safe over-estimate.

Minimum Sample Sizes – Attribute (Discrete) Data

For Attribute Data, calculate the minimum sample size as follows:

The Process

↓

Estimate the proportion of the process (p) – see opposite.

↓

Decide on the precision that you require (d)

↓

Calculate the minimum sample size (MSS) as follows:

$$MSS = (2 / d)^2 * p * (1-p)$$

If the minimum sample size exceeds the parts available, measure them all (100%)

Example: Collecting data to assess the proportion of furniture flat packs that are sold with parts missing.
NB: Unit is one flat pack

↓

Historically you estimate the proportion is around 10% (expressed as 0.10)

↓

Required precision = +/- 1.5% (expressed as 0.015)

↓

$$MSS = (2 / 0.015)^2 * 0.1 * (1-0.1)$$

$$= 1600$$

So to estimate the proportion of flat packs sold with parts missing to within +/- 1.5%, you should collect at least 1600 pieces of data.

Estimating process proportion:

Knowing the expected proportion in the process (p) helps to achieve a more realistic sample size.

But how do you know the expected proportion when you haven't even measured the process yet? – you estimate it.

Remember, it's just an estimate. If you later find it to be inaccurate, you can always recalculate your MSS.

❗ This sample size is significantly larger than the previous (continuous data) example. This reflects the lower 'resolution' and quality of the Attribute data world, as discussed on page 44.

Minimum Sample Sizes – Summary

Minimum sample sizes are just that – a *minimum* level that should be used as a sense check.

Where the minimum sample size can be used:

Minimum sample sizes are just a starting point for use in basic Six Sigma tools such as Histograms, Capability Studies and Sigma Levels. More advanced techniques such as SPC charts and Hypothesis Testing may require larger sample sizes.

The approaches explained in the previous pages can be used as a sense check when designing data collection plans during the Measure phase.

Firstly, calculate your minimum sample size then choose your data collection strategy, and then keep collecting data until you reach the minimum sample size *before* you make any calculations or decisions with the data.

Applying minimum sample sizes in reality:

In reality, the amount of data you have access to, and the time and resources you have available can prevent you reaching the minimum sample size.

For example, if it takes 1 hour to collect one piece of Attribute data (pass/fail) for a specific product or service, then it could take several months to reach your minimum sample size.

Instead you could try and measure Continuous or Count data from the process since these are 'richer' data worlds and require smaller samples.

What if you cannot get enough data to meet the minimum sample size?

Use what you have got, but with the awareness that your confidence in any statistics or decisions generated from the data will be lower than you would like it to be.

Confidence Intervals can be used to assess the precision of a statistic – see page 125 for more details.

What if I have much *more* data than my minimum sample size?

Don't complain! – but also check that you are not investing valuable resources in collecting unnecessarily large amounts of data.

It might be possible to reduce the amount of data being collected without compromising on the level of precision you require.

Sampling Frequency

Having decided to measure a process using a sampling approach, you will need to decide when and where to sample the process – **'sampling frequency'**.

Selecting the frequency with which to monitor your process:

Every process has some level of expected 'cycles' in its output. For example:

- for a process operating across 3 shifts, the duration of the expected cycles could be around 8 hours.
- for a machining process, the tool wear might create an expected cycle duration of only a few hours.
- for an accounting process, the expected cycle duration might be around a week, to align with known procedures and systems that are in place.

Using this information, the sampling frequency should be arranged to be at least 4 times every cycle, in order that process changes "within" the expected cycles will be reflected in the data collected, as shown below.

Process Output

Expected Process "Cycle"

Minimum frequency – 4 times every process cycle

Sampling from Population:

A statistically "sound" approach to sampling is important when sampling a population in order to ensure the sample is representative.

A completely **random** approach gives the whole population an equal chance of being selected.

Alternatively, it may be important to ensure that specific categories within a population are represented in a sample. A **stratified** sampling approach involves randomly selecting data from specific categories **within** a population.

For example, a completely *random* approach to court jury selection may not produce exactly 6 men and 6 women.

A *stratified* approach would be to deliberately select 6 women and 6 men in order to ensure that the male/female ratio of the population is reflected in the jury.

Contextual Data – The 4ᵗʰ Data World

Categorical data provides information on the context from which a particular piece of data was taken. This information is essential later on in the Analyse phase of a Six Sigma project.

The spreadsheet shown here is typical of real data – it contains data on a fault repair process.

The first three columns demonstrate how the **output** of the process might be recorded in the three 'data worlds'.

The remainder of the data columns contain **'contextual'** information about the fault repairs, and are mostly **categorical** in nature.

Why is contextual data important?

Contextual data is essential during the analyse phase of a project. Without it, you will have trouble looking for clues in the data. It is therefore important to record as much contextual information about process events as possible.

You can always decide not to use the data later on, but it is difficult to go back and find contextual data after the event.

Numerical Data
representing the process output

Categorical / Contextual Data
Representing the 'background' of each piece of data

A variety of categorical information – some numeric, some textual, and some mixed.

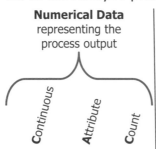

Time taken to complete	Final result	No. of defects found	ID	Type	Technology	Location	Skills required	Priority
23.2	Pass	0	W182	Com	1	SW	Manual	Low
27.5	Pass	0	W183	Direct	1	N	Skilled-W	Med
28.3	Pass	0	W184	Com	2	SW	Skilled-D	Low
29.5	Fail	1	W185	Direct	3	S	Clerical	High
30.8	Pass	0	W186	Direct	1	N	Skilled-W	High
28.1	Fail	2	W187	Group	2	S	Manual	Med
29.9	Pass	0	W188	Group	2	SW	Skilled-D	Low
	Fail	1	W189	Com			Skilled-D	High

Minitab is case sensitive, so contextual pieces of data may not be recognised as the same if they are not spelt in **exactly** the same way.

Measurement System Analysis (MSA)

Too many business problems are analysed with data that is known to be suspect. If the data is poor quality, there is no option but to stop and fix it during the Measure phase of a project.

What is a Measurement System?

A measurement system is not just a device such as a ruler or timer but it includes the people, standards, and procedures that surround the measurement process itself.

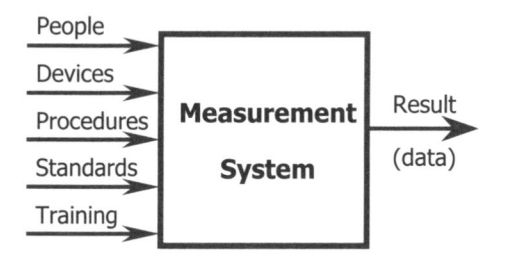

Why is this relevant?

The data in our spreadsheets may not faithfully reflect the process data because it has been through a Measurement System which could have introduced errors and bias to the data.

Measurement System Analysis refers to a range of techniques that can help to identify the sources of error in our data.

Example: Imagine a process that takes 20 minutes on average with a range from 10-30. The distribution curve on the right shows what we should see when we measure and plot the data. This is referred to as the **'truth'**.

The four plots below represent the range of actual results that might be provided by the measurement system. The top left picture is the only one that represents the 'truth'. The other three exhibit mixtures of errors that can be categorised into two themes - Precision and Bias (see p55).

The 'Truth'

Measurement System Analysis Routemap

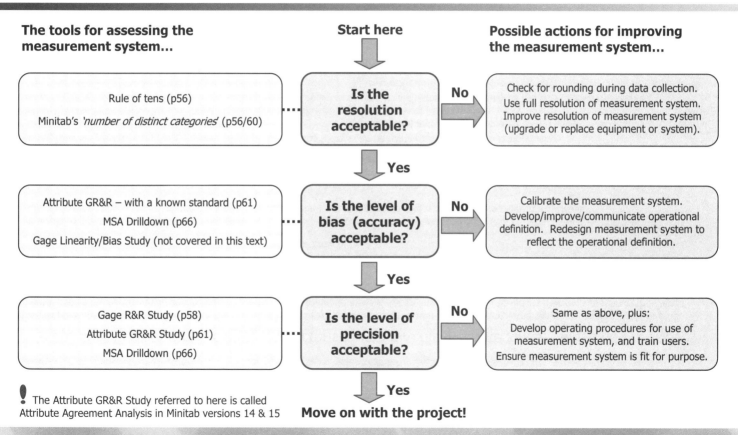

The tools for assessing the measurement system...

Start here

Possible actions for improving the measurement system...

| Rule of tens (p56)
Minitab's *number of distinct categories* (p56/60) | ┈┈ | **Is the resolution acceptable?** | **No** → | Check for rounding during data collection.
Use full resolution of measurement system.
Improve resolution of measurement system (upgrade or replace equipment or system). |

Yes

| Attribute GR&R – with a known standard (p61)
MSA Drilldown (p66)
Gage Linearity/Bias Study (not covered in this text) | ┈┈ | **Is the level of bias (accuracy) acceptable?** | **No** → | Calibrate the measurement system.
Develop/improve/communicate operational definition. Redesign measurement system to reflect the operational definition. |

Yes

| Gage R&R Study (p58)
Attribute GR&R Study (p61)
MSA Drilldown (p66) | ┈┈ | **Is the level of precision acceptable?** | **No** → | Same as above, plus:
Develop operating procedures for use of measurement system, and train users.
Ensure measurement system is fit for purpose. |

Yes

Move on with the project!

❗ The Attribute GR&R Study referred to here is called Attribute Agreement Analysis in Minitab versions 14 & 15

Sources of Measurement Error – Bias and Precision

Measurement System errors can be characterised into two distinct categories – Bias and Precision.

Bias errors are consistent types of error that do not increase the variation you see in your results, but do shift the data so that results are consistently higher or lower than they should be. For example:

- a ruler has 20mm missing from the end, so it is consistently giving results 20mm too long

- your bathroom scales are not set up correctly and consistently over estimate your weight by 3 kilos.

- the start time for resolving a customer complaint is consistently recorded 20 minutes **after** the customer first called (i.e. too late!)

Assessing Bias errors can be done through Attribute Agreement Studies (p61), MSA Drilldowns (p66) and Gauge Linearity and Bias Studies (see Minitab)

Fixing Bias errors is achieved through solutions such as routine calibration, limiting the allowable operating range of a gauge, training, and using visual standards, etc.

Precision errors are those that do not happen in the same way all the time – in other words they add more variation into the data. This means that the variation in the data is more than is actually in the process. For example:

- some people measure from the end of a ruler and others start from the point at which zero is marked.

- your bathroom scales only have markings every 5 kilos, so that you have to (not very reliably) guess the last few kilos every time you measure yourself.

- the start time for a customer complaint could be anything from 5-20 minutes after the customer first called, depending on operator training, workload, experience, breaks etc.

'Precision' errors can be further divided into two categories:

1) Repeatability: Variations caused by the gauge itself (and as a result of its ease of use) are called Repeatability errors, since they refer to the ability of a gauge to provide repeatable measurements if all other factors (such as the user) are held constant.

2) Reproducibility: Differences in the ways in which different people carry out a measurement are called Reproducibility errors, since they refer to the ability of people to reproduce the results of their colleagues (if all other factors are held constant).

Assessing Precision errors can be done through Gauge R&R Studies (p58), Attribute Agreement Studies (p61) and MSA Drilldowns (p66)

Fixing Precision errors is achieved through solutions such as developing operational definitions and working standards, training, improving gauge resolution, and sometimes changing the gauge in use.

Measurement System Resolution

If the resolution is too large to allow effective discrimination of the process variation then failing the GR&R test is inevitable. Checking resolution is a simple practical tool that is worth doing first.

Resolution: The smallest units within the data represent the resolution of the measurement system.   So, the resolution of data sets 1 and 2 below, is 0.05 and 1 respectively.

78
85
94
91
89
81
88
92
79
87

5.00
4.95
4.90
5.05
5.15
4.95
5.00
4.80
4.95
5.10

Data Set 1
Resolution: 0.05
Min: 4.80
Max: 5.15
Range: 0.35

Data Set 2
Resolution: 1
Min: 78
Max: 94
Range: 16

What causes poor resolution?

▪ Often it is because the system or gauge is not capable of any finer measurements. In this case, upgrading the system/gauge is inevitable.

▪ Sometimes however, you will find that data is being rounded at some point in the collection process.

The 'Rule of Tens' says that the resolution of your gauge should be able to fit ten times into the process variation you are measuring, as shown below.

Process Variation

Applying the Rule of Tens is a quick practical tool for assessing if the measurement system has any hope of passing the GR&R test. For example:

▪ Data Set 1 (left) has a resolution of 0.05.   The process variation can be estimated by the range of the data to be 0.35 (=5.15-4.80).

The resolution (0.05) only divides into the process variation (0.35) seven times, and so the measurement system employed is unlikely to be acceptable, and fails the 'rule of tens'.

▪ The resolution of data set 2 appears more acceptable. The resolution is 1, and the process range (variation) is 16, meaning that it comfortably passes the 'rule of tens'.

Minitab's equivalent measure of resolution is called the **'number of distinct categories'** (see page 60). The concept is the same but the calculations involved are slightly different, and so the criteria for acceptability is 5 or more (not 10 as described here).

GR&R – Gauge Repeatability and Reproducibility

GR&R studies quantify the Precision errors of a measurement system to determine its acceptability.

A GR&R Study measures precision error by taking one part and measuring it several times with several different people.

Given that the part is not changing in size, any variation in the results must represent the Repeatability of the gauge and the Reproducibility of measurements by different people. This is abbreviated to 'GR&R'.

A GR&R study repeats this approach on several different parts to assess the results.

One part, measured many times, gives a range of results that represent the "GR&R":

Average result

GR&R Variation Shown for comparison purposes.

What is an acceptable level of GR&R variation? It is not the absolute level of GR&R that is important, but the relative level. For example, the timer that is used for measuring the finish time of a marathon would not be acceptable for measuring the 100 metres sprint. Similarly the volt meter used to measure household electrics would not be acceptable for measuring voltages across electronic components.   In other words, a measurement system must be 'fit for purpose'.

So, the acceptability of GR&R variation is assessed on the **ratio** (expressed as a percentage) of the GR&R variation compared to the process (part to part) variation **and** the customer tolerance, as shown below:

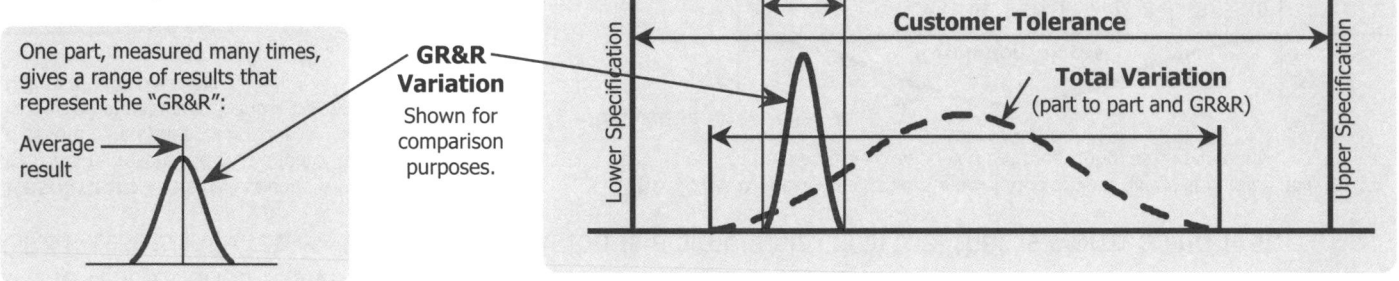

GR&R Acceptability Criteria:	Marginal	Good	Excellent
GR&R as a percentage of the Total Variation = GR&R / Total Variation * 100%	<30%	<20%	<10%
GR&R as a percentage of the Tolerance = GR&R / Tolerance * 100%	<30%	<20%	<10%

Continuous GR&R in Minitab – Data Input

A common standard for a GR&R study is to use 10 parts, measured by 3 different people, 3 times each, providing a total of 90 results.

Data Preparation: As usual, Minitab requires the data in columns; one for the part number, one for the appraiser and one for the measurement result, as shown below.

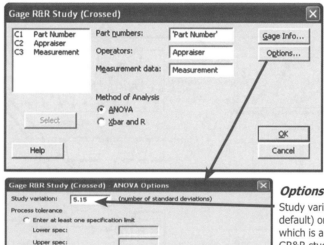

Minitab: Stat > Quality Tools > (Gage Study V14 and V15) > Gage R&R Study (Crossed)

	C1	C2	C3
	Part Number	Appraiser	Measurement
1	1	1	1.65
2	1	1	1.60
3	1	1	1.70
4	2	1	2.00
5	2	1	2.00
6	2	1	2.00
7	3	1	1.85
8	3	1	1.80
9	3	1	1.85
10	4	1	1.85
11	4	1	1.95
12	4	1	1.90
13	5	1	1.55
14	5	1	1.45
15	5	1	1.55

❗ The order of the rows doesn't matter, as long as the data is matched across the columns.

Example: A project is looking at controlling the thickness of steel from a rolling process.

A GR&R study for the measurement system has been completed on 10 pieces of steel, using three different appraisers.

The three key data inputs are self explanatory. Note that the part number and appraiser can be textual data (such as the names of the appraisers).

Options:

Study variation can be left at 6 (which is the Minitab default) or changed to 5.15 (as shown here) – which is a common industrial standard for use in GR&R studies.

The **process tolerance** is optional but must be completed if you require GR&R as a percentage of tolerance. Minitab 15 allows you to enter either the **actual** specifications or the difference between them (the **total** tolerance), which in this example is 1.0mm (because the specification is +/-0.5mm).

 "GR&R-Crossed.mpj"

Continuous GR&R in Minitab – Graphical Output

The top left graph is the primary output for analysis.

The **Gage GR&R** group of columns should be small in comparison to the **Part-to-Part** group of columns.

- The first column in the GR&R group deals with **% Contribution** and is not a metric discussed here.

- The second column in the GR&R group shows the GR&R as a **% of Study Variation** (Total Variation).

- The third column in the GR&R group shows GR&R as a **% of Tolerance**. If you don't have this column it's because you didn't enter a Tolerance under '**Options**'.

The middle two sets of columns represent the sub-components of the GR&R group separately (i.e. Repeatability and Reproducibility).

This example shows that Reproducibility is the larger component of GR&R, indicating that improvements should focus on reducing the differences **between** appraisers first.

GR&R of Sheet Metal Thickness using Gage #5050

If the GR&R is too high, then the graphs on the right can be used to investigate why.

The top chart shows all the results for each part in order (1–10) to see if particular parts were difficult to measure. In this case part 10 has very variable results.

The second chart helps to show reproducibility by showing all the results by appraiser. In this case appraiser 2 has lower measurements (on average) than the others, which might be worth investigating.

The third chart is the same as the top, but separates out the results by appraiser.

The two lower left charts are effectively SPC charts (p195).

The middle chart is checking for unlikely results that might be a result of a special cause occurring during the GR&R exercise. If any of the points are outside of the red lines, check that there were no specific problems with that part and that there were no typing mistakes when entering the data.

In contrast, the bottom chart **should** have lots of points outside of the control lines, which indicates the GR&R % is low, so don't worry if your graph looks like this one.

Continuous GR&R in Minitab – Session Window Output

Gage R&R Study - ANOVA Method

Two-Way ANOVA Table With Interaction

Source	DF	SS	MS	F	P
Part Number	9	2.92322	0.324802	36.5530	0.000
Appraiser	2	0.06339	0.031694	3.5669	0.050
Part Number * Appraiser	18	0.15994	0.008886	8.8858	0.000
Repeatability	60	0.06000	0.001000		
Total	89	3.20656			

Gage R&R

Source	VarComp	%Contribution (of VarComp)
Total Gage R&R	0.0043889	11.11
Repeatability	0.0010000	2.53
Reproducibility	0.0033889	8.58
Appraiser	0.0007603	1.93
Appraiser*Part Number	0.0026286	6.66
Part-To-Part	0.0351019	88.89
Total Variation	0.0394907	100.00

Source	StdDev (SD)	Study Var (5.15 * SD)	%Study Var (%SV)	%Tolerance (SV/Toler)
Total Gage R&R	0.066249	0.34118	33.34	34.12
Repeatability	0.031623	0.16286	15.91	16.29
Reproducibility	0.058214	0.29980	29.29	29.98
Appraiser	0.027573	0.14200	13.88	14.20
Appraiser*Part Number	0.051270	0.26404	25.80	26.40
Part-To-Part	0.187355	0.96488	94.28	96.49
Total Variation	0.198723	1.02342	100.00	102.34

Number of Distinct Categories = 3

There is a lot of session window output from a GR&R study, but most of it just repeats the message contained within the graphs.

The ANOVA table is used to assess which sources of variation are statistically significant. In this case, the appraiser **does** have an affect on the result and there is an interaction between Part Number and Appraisers, because both the p-values are 0.05 or less. See pages 129/130 for an explanation of p-values.

This second set of data represents the GR&R in terms of its contribution towards variance and is not explored further in this text.

The third set of data (below) provides the detail behind the top left graph of the graphical output (previous page), as follows:

Graphically the GR&R looked 'high' (see previous page) and it is quantified here as being 33.34% of the Total Variation and 34.12% of the Tolerance. Both these results are above 30% and therefore indicate improvement is required in the measurement system.

The Graphical results also indicated that Reproducibility was a larger component of GR&R than Repeatability. The figures here support this, showing that Reproducibility factors (at approx 29%) are contributing twice the variation that Repeatability factors are (approx 16%).

This number represents the Number of Distinct Categories that the measurement system is capable of discriminating within the process variation present. The target is more than 5, and so the result of 3 here also indicates the measurement system needs improvement. See page 56 for more on gauge resolution.

Attribute GR&R (Attribute Agreement Analysis in Minitab)

All the same principles of GR&R can be applied to the Attribute data world as well. The target for an Attribute MSA is for it to reach the correct decision, every time.

Attribute GR&Rs are conducted in almost identical fashion to those for Continuous data.   Several different appraisers are asked to decide the acceptability of several different products (or services), each several different times. The results are used to assess the **reproducibility** (how well the appraisers agree with each other) as well as the **repeatability** (how consistently they agree with themselves).

The key differences of Attribute data GR&R studies are:
- More data is required, (because the Attribute data world has less resolution). At least 20 parts should be assessed at least 3 times by each appraiser.
- You should ensure your selection of parts includes some borderline products or services that will really challenge the ability of the measurement system.

Part Number	Tom - 1	Tom - 2	Tom - 3	Dick - 1	Dick - 2	Dick - 3	Harry - 1	Harry - 2	Harry - 3	Experts Decis
1	Accept	Accept	Accept	Accept	Accept	Accept	Accept	Accept	Accept	Accept
2	Reject	Reject	Reject	Reject	Reject	Reject	Reject	Reject	Reject	Reject
3	Accept	Reject	Accept	Accept	Accept	Accept	Accept	Accept	Accept	Accept
4	Accept	Accept	Accept	Accept	Accept	Accept	Accept	Accept	Accept	Accept
5	Accept	Reject	Reject	Accept	Accept	Accept	Accept	Accept	Accept	Accept
6	Accept	Accept	Accept	Accept	Accept	Accept	Accept	Accept	Accept	Accept
7	Accept	Accept	Accept	Accept	Accept	Accept	Accept	Accept	Accept	Accept

Tom's Results   Dick's Results   Harry's Results

Bias can also occur in an attribute measurement system. Even if all the appraisers reach a unanimous decision that a product/service is acceptable – in other words they have perfect 'GR&R' – it might be that they are all making the wrong decision – 'bias'.

The Attribute GR&R in Minitab allows bias to be assessed at the same time as GR&R. In order to do this, the 'correct' decision for each part number must be known and entered in a separate column, as shown on the left.

Because of the often subjective nature of Attribute measurements, it is not always easy to determine what the correct decision is. One approach is to ask a group of 'experts' (perhaps the process owner, engineer, or the customer) what their consensus decision is, and to define this as the 'truth' (as shown here in the last column).

This selection of data is taken from the example data file used in the following pages, and specified below.

A first glance reveals that rows 1, 2, 4, 6 & 7 have perfect GR&R and no bias, because all the appraisers agreed with the 'expert' all the time.

However, rows 3 and 5 (highlighted) show that Tom had problems repeating his own decisions on those parts.

💾 **"GR&R-Attribute.mpj"**

Attribute GR&R – Data Input

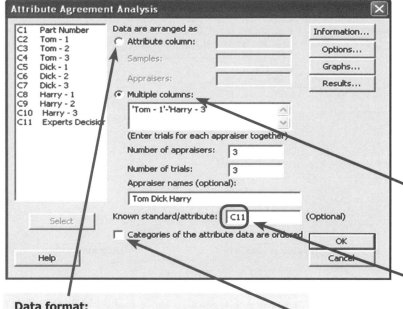

In version 13, this function can be found under:
Stat > Quality Tools > Attribute Gage R&R Study

In versions 14 and 15, it is located under:
Stat > Quality Tools > Attribute Agreement Analysis

For most purposes within Six Sigma projects, the Attribute Agreement Study shown here is perfectly suitable – particularly in service and transactional environments.

Note that versions 14 & 15 also has a similar technique called Attribute Gauge Study (Analytical Method). However, this technique is more complex and is beyond the scope here.

Using the 'Multiple Columns' option, all the columns for one appraiser must be next to each other. Minitab then knows to take the first three columns of your selection and assign them to the same appraiser

If you have a column containing the 'correct' or 'expert's' decision, enter it here in order for Minitab to estimate the bias within the results.

Data format:

If you have all of your results (decisions) stored in a single column, with two additional columns for the sample number and appraiser, then use the **"Attribute Column"** option.

The example in use here has the data across '**Multiple Columns'** which is an easier format to view.

The example here only deals with Attribute data, although this function can also deal with ordinal data (where the results have a natural ranking to them) by checking this box. See Minitab Help for more information.

Attribute GR&R – Graphical Output

Assessment Agreement

Date of study :
Reported by :
Name of product :
Misc :

Appraiser vs Standard Because there was an 'expert' decision (a '*known standard*'), the graphical output also shows the performance of the appraisers against that standard.

For example;

- Tom only agreed with the 'expert' decision on 80% of the parts

- Dick (who had a perfect score in terms of repeating his own decisions), agreed with the standard around 95% of the time.

If the appraiser did not agree with the standard then either the part was appraised as good but defined as bad by the expert, or vice versa. The results in the **session window** (see the next page) provide more detail on this (and all the exact calculations behind these graphs).

The **Within Appraiser** results show the **repeatability** of the appraisers as a percentage score. The dot indicates the actual calculation, whilst the lines extending in either direction indicate the (95%) confidence intervals for the result.

Confidence intervals are used because a sample size of 20 or 30 parts is not very large when dealing with Attribute data (p43).

- So, Tom reached the same decision on 90% of the parts, (but the confidence interval indicates this could be anywhere from approx 73% to 97%).

- Dick reached the same decision on all of the parts (100%).

Where to focus improvement:

Low '*within appraiser*' scores would indicate a need to help the appraisers reach consistent decisions – maybe through improved inspection conditions etc.

Low '*appraiser versus standard*' scores would indicate the need to provide better operational definitions on the acceptability criteria of the product/service, supported by visual standards and training where necessary.

Attribute GR&R – Session Window Output

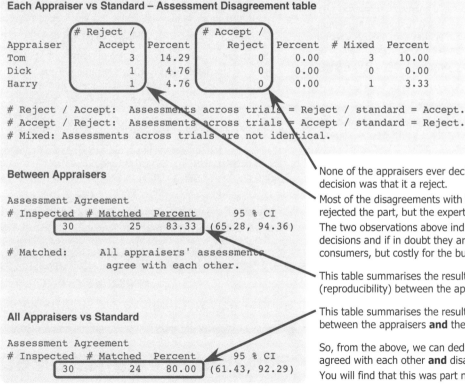

Each Appraiser vs Standard – Assessment Disagreement table

Appraiser	# Reject / Accept	Percent	# Accept / Reject	Percent	# Mixed	Percent
Tom	3	14.29	0	0.00	3	10.00
Dick	1	4.76	0	0.00	0	0.00
Harry	1	4.76	0	0.00	1	3.33

```
# Reject / Accept:  Assessments across trials = Reject / standard = Accept.
# Accept / Reject:  Assessments across trials = Accept / standard = Reject.
# Mixed: Assessments across trials are not identical.
```

Between Appraisers

```
Assessment Agreement
# Inspected  # Matched  Percent      95 % CI
    30           25      83.33   (65.28, 94.36)

# Matched:      All appraisers' assessment
                agree with each other.
```

All Appraisers vs Standard

```
Assessment Agreement
# Inspected  # Matched  Percent      95 % CI
    30           24      80.00   (61.43, 92.29)
```

Minitab's session window output for the Attribute Agreement Analysis function contains a substantial amount of data. The first two sections repeat the data shown in the graphical output (previous page) and are therefore **not** shown here.

The remainder of the output is shown here (but without the Fleiss' Kappa Statistics, which are not dealt with in this text).

The Assessment Disagreement provides detail on **how** the appraisers disagreed with the 'expert' decision (standard). For example:

None of the appraisers ever decided that a part was acceptable, when the experts decision was that it a reject.

Most of the disagreements with the standard occurred when the appraisers rejected the part, but the experts decision was that the part was acceptable.

The two observations above indicate that appraisers are being cautious in their decisions and if in doubt they are rejecting parts – a good, safe approach for consumers, but costly for the business!

This table summarises the results by showing that there was **complete** agreement (reproducibility) between the appraisers on only 25 of the 30 parts (83%).

This table summarises the results by showing that there was complete agreement between the appraisers **and** the standard on only 24 of the 30 parts (80%).

So, from the above, we can deduce that for one of the parts, **all** of the appraisers agreed with each other **and** disagreed with the standard at the same time! You will find that this was part number (and row number) 25 in the data file.

GR&R Studies in Practice

GR&R studies are experiments that require careful control in order to ensure they provide valid results.

Conducting GR&R Studies

A GR&R study is effectively an experiment in which components of the measurement system are adjusted in a controlled manner. As an experiment, careful planning is required to ensure the results are statistically valid:

▪ Select the sample parts at random and run the trial in a completely random order.

▪ Ensure the parts represent the full operating range of the process – i.e. its long term variation. This can be done by collecting the parts over an extended time period.

▪ Complete the study in standard operating conditions. In other words:
   - use the same appraisers as usual
   - do not train the appraisers before hand – you want to measure the effectiveness of the **existing** system.
   - conduct the experiment in the same location as normal

▪ Ensure that the study is "Blind"
   - this means that the appraisers should not be aware of the part number that they are measuring or be able to remember their last measurement. This is difficult if the parts have numbers written on them!

This is all a lot to ask! – so make sure you have a facilitator for the study who controls the conditions and is aware of the statistical rigour required.

Within Part Variation

All physical parts have levels of 'within part variation' in them. If you measured the diameter of a football in different places there would be some differences in the results because the ball would not be perfectly round.

Unfortunately, a GR&R exercise would wrongly attribute the variation within a part to that of GR&R error, since the GR&R process assumes the parts are perfectly consistent.

Whilst it may be a practical problem if the football is not round, it is not an issue of measurement error and so needs to be removed from the experiment. The solution is to specify a point on the ball that the measurement must be taken at (for the purpose of the GR&R experiment).

GR&R with Destructive Testing or One-off events

In certain situations, a measurement cannot be repeated. The tensile strength of a metal sample for example, cannot be repeated because it is destroyed the first time. The solution to this is the GR&R (Nested) function found in Minitab.

This advanced technique relies on the careful selection of parts so that small batches of parts that have been taken close together can be assumed to have identical properties. The batches are then selected at different times in order that the longer term process variation will be present between them.

This technique is not detailed further here and would require experienced support in its use.

'MSA Drilldown'

Even if GR&R studies cannot be applied in their purest form, you must be confident that your data represents what it is supposed to. 'MSA Drilldowns' are a method for doing that.

What is an MSA Drilldown?

An MSA Drilldown is a structured approach to checking the quality of your data. Its principle is that you should not be using data if you do not know where it came from, and so an MSA Drilldown helps to challenge the "pedigree" of the data. A 'tree' diagram is the best way to structure the results, as shown on the right.

The key steps are:

Drilldown through the data to find its source components

↓

Challenge each component in terms of possible measurement error – bias or precision

↓

For each potential source or error, decide if its acceptable (within context)

↓

If it is acceptable, then document your decision and move on with the project

Measurement: Time to resolve customer complaint.

Start Time

Call centre operator hits submit button on complaint logging form.

What about customer waiting time to call centre? (bias)

Complaint log is left open until 'diagnostic' work is complete – up to 2 hours (precision)

Some operators leave logs open and submit them in groups to save time (precision)

Stop Time

Operator closes log

Manager closes log if complaint has been escalated – (precision)

Some operators close immediately, some close at end of day (precision)

Useful questions during an MSA Drilldown:

- Where does the data come from? ("a database" is not acceptable – how does it get there?).
- How is it collected and what triggers it to be collected? (the press of a button, manual recording, barcode scanning?)
- Are there different people or systems collecting the same data?

Distribution Shapes and the Normal Distribution

The Normal distribution is a common and useful statistical model, but it is not the end of the world! Continuous data that is *not* Normal (big N) is still useful data and it is still normal (little n!).

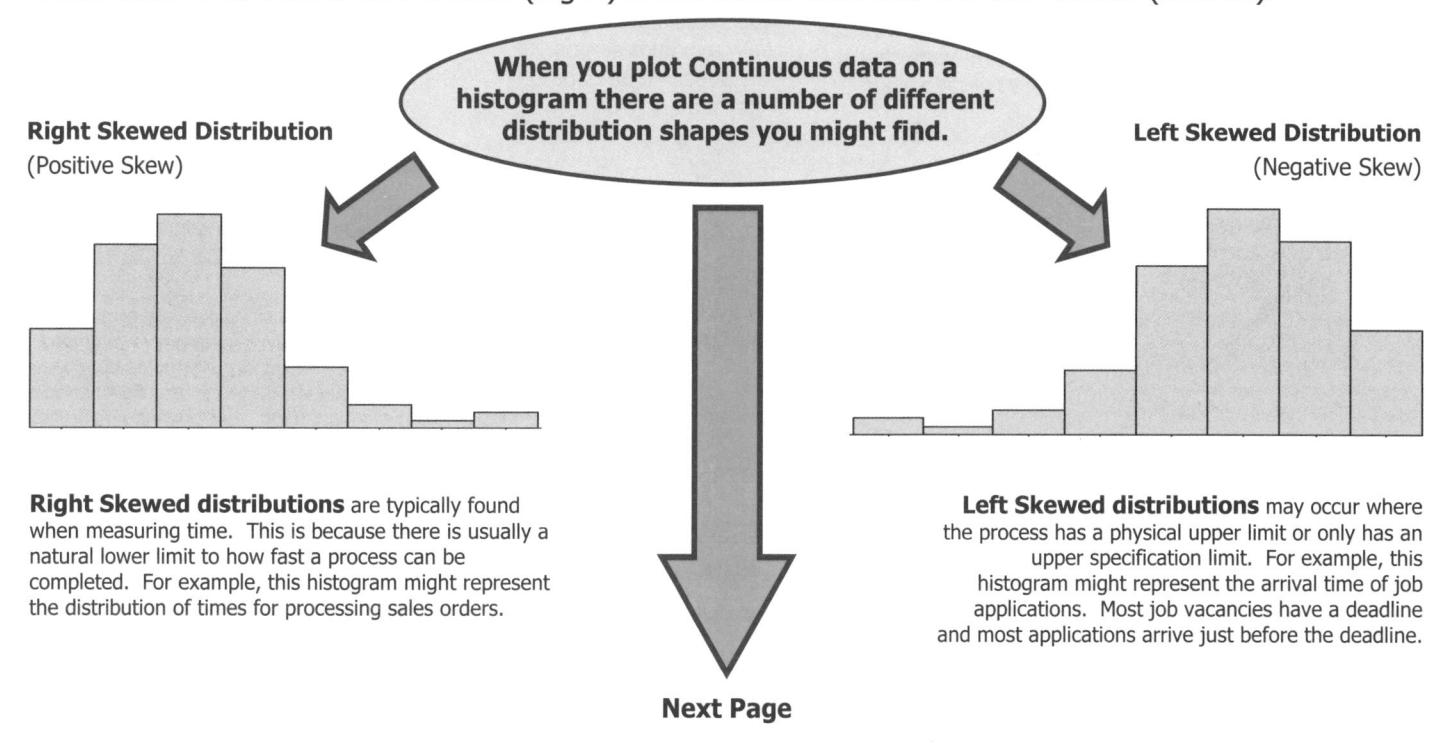

When you plot Continuous data on a histogram there are a number of different distribution shapes you might find.

Right Skewed Distribution
(Positive Skew)

Left Skewed Distribution
(Negative Skew)

Right Skewed distributions are typically found when measuring time. This is because there is usually a natural lower limit to how fast a process can be completed. For example, this histogram might represent the distribution of times for processing sales orders.

Left Skewed distributions may occur where the process has a physical upper limit or only has an upper specification limit. For example, this histogram might represent the arrival time of job applications. Most job vacancies have a deadline and most applications arrive just before the deadline.

Next Page

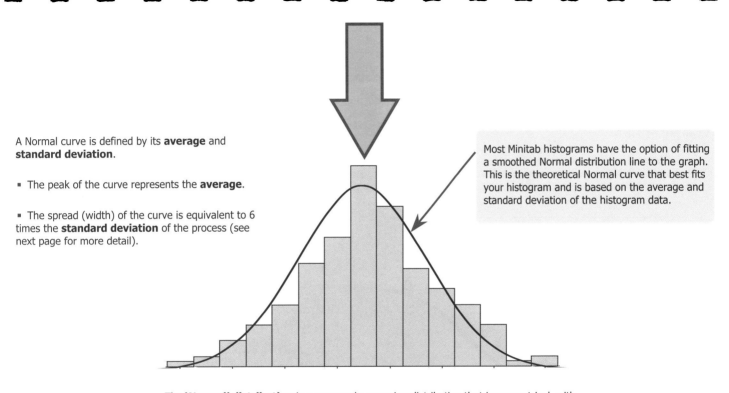

A Normal curve is defined by its **average** and **standard deviation**.

- The peak of the curve represents the **average**.

- The spread (width) of the curve is equivalent to 6 times the **standard deviation** of the process (see next page for more detail).

Most Minitab histograms have the option of fitting a smoothed Normal distribution line to the graph. This is the theoretical Normal curve that best fits your histogram and is based on the average and standard deviation of the histogram data.

The **'Normal' distribution** is a commonly occurring distribution that is symmetrical, with most of the results in the middle and fewer towards the extremes. It is also sometimes called a bell shaped curve, or Gaussian curve. Remember that 'Normal' is a name, so it has a capital N.

See the next page to find out more about the Normal distribution.
See page 159 to find out how to decide if your data follows the Normal distribution.

The Normal Distribution in Theory

In theory the Normal distribution never ends but in practice most results fall within +/- 3 Sigmas.

Standard Deviations and the Normal distribution:

A wider-flatter histogram demonstrates more variation in the process and therefore a higher standard deviation (vice versa for a narrower-taller histogram).

In theory, the Normal curve actually carries on forever, making it possible (but very unlikely) to have extreme results from time to time. However, for all intents and purposes, 100% of the results are contained within 3 standard deviations either side of the average – a total of Six Sigmas.

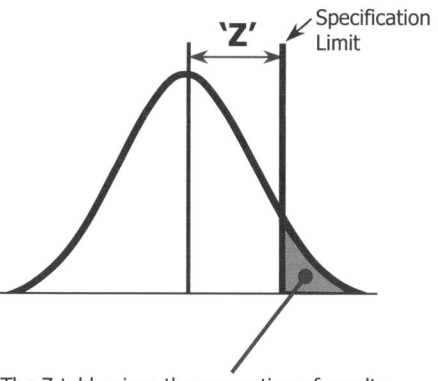

The Z-table gives the proportion of results that will be outside the limit, based on the distance 'Z' between the average and the limit, *in standard deviations.*

The Z-Table: The shape of the Normal curve dictates that most of the results will be towards the centre of the distribution. In fact, as shown above, 68% of the results will be within +/- 1 Sigma of the average.   The complex shape of the Normal curve has been converted into a mathematical table called the Z-table.

The Z-table provides the proportion of results that will fall outside of a specific limit, as shown on the left.   All that is required is the distance 'Z' between the average and the limit in question.

The important point is that the distance 'Z' must be defined in terms of how many standard deviations it represents.

An abbreviated Z-table can be found inside the back cover of this guide. Alternatively, a full interactive Z-table is contained in the data file: **"Z-Table & Sigma Levels.xls"**

The Normal Distribution in Practice

If the Normal distribution is applicable, it can be used to estimate future process performance.

1: A CD manufacturer has had problems producing CDs within the maximum thickness specification of 1.5mm. They are testing a new production machine that they hope will produce better CD products. A test run of 100 CDs has been made and the thickness results look like this:

Average = 1.35
Std Dev. = 0.06

Upper Spec Limit = 1.5mm

2: None of the 100 test CDs were above the upper spec limit of 1.5mm so it appears that the machine will not make any oversize CDs. However, the Normal curve on the histogram still extends beyond the 1.5mm limit, which suggests that over the longer term (500,000 CDs later!) some of the CDs will be oversize.

3: Since the histogram appears to fit the Normal curve, the Normal distribution can be used to make a better prediction of the number of failures that will occur in the long term.

The Z-table (inside back cover) provides the area under the Normal curve outside of an upper specification limit, but it requires the distance between the average and the specification limit *in standard deviations (not mm),* as shown below:

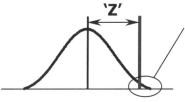

'Z'

The Z-table provides the area under the curve that is outside of the limit.

The data file for this example is contained within:

💾 **"Capability-CD.mpj"**

4: So for this case:

$$Z = \frac{\text{Upper Spec. Limit} - \text{Average}}{\text{Standard Deviation}} = \frac{(1.5 - 1.35)}{0.06} = 2.5$$

The Z-table predicts the area under the curve to be 0.6% for a Z-value of 2.5. This is different (and a better prediction than) the 0% predicted by looking at the **actual** test run of 100.

'1st Pass Analysis' – Time Series Plots and Histograms

Although not in the Analyse phase yet, a '1st pass analysis' of the KPIs during the Measure phase provides a baseline as well as an understanding of the current process behaviour.

Time Series plots and Histograms are the primary graphical tools of Six Sigma. They work together to provide an understanding of process performance.

Example 3

Example 1 – Time Series plot

Example 2

Time Series Plots (see p109):
At this point, do not read too much into small changes, trends or patterns. Instead, we are looking for any obvious changes that have occurred in the past, like:

This process has a definite trend upwards and a repeating pattern as well.

This process appears to have had a significant step change in the past, and now appears to be decreasing.

Example 1 – histogram

Frequency

50 60 70 80 90 100

Histograms (see p104) A histogram summarises the overall performance of a process and shows the shape of the distribution. Again, do not read too much into the graphical results at this point, we are looking for general observations.

So, for example 1 (left), a general observation is that the process appears to be centred symmetrically around 80 (approx.).

A **'1st Pass Analysis'** (histogram and Time Series plot) should be completed for each KPI at this stage of the project.

Any baseline figures that are quoted in the **problem statement** should be clearly indicated as shown here by the dashed lines.

Process Stability (common and special cause variation)

A common phrase in terms of summarising the behaviour of a process is 'stability'. Understanding whether a process is 'stable' or not has implications for the ways in which it might be controlled.

A stable process has stable inputs. The key concept behind 'process stability' is that the variation of the output of a process is dependant on the type of variation in its inputs.

▪ A stable process is one where all of its inputs are varying in a random way. Combining together, these **'common cause'** variations create a similarly random variation in the output, that is predictable within certain limits.

▪ An unstable process is one where one or more of its inputs are behaving in an extremely unpredictable way. The resulting output variation can therefore be assigned to **'special cause'** variation, but cannot be predicted.

A common example of special cause variation is the weather. A lightning strike might create a 'special cause' surge of several thousand volts in mains voltage that normally varies in a relatively stable manner.

How to assess process stability: In order to help detect signs of instability in a process that might not be easily spotted by the human eye, SPC charts can be used in the Measure phase to analyse historical process data. **SPC charts** are an advanced form of Time Series plot, and are described in detail on page 195.

A Stable Process... is **in-control** and **predictable**, and its output varies due to **'common cause'** variation in all of its inputs.

An Unstable Process... is **out of control** and **unpredictable,** and its output varies due to **'special cause'** variation in just one or two of its inputs, that tend to dominate the process.

Some examples:

This process appears to be stable. There are no obvious 'outliers' or trends, and so this output variation is a reasonable prediction of future performance.

This process appears to be stable with the exception of two outliers. These should be investigated to determine their 'special causes'.

This process is clearly not stable over time. The process changes should be investigated to establish if the special causes were controlled or deliberate changes to the process.

Short and Long Term Variation

The difference between short term and long term process stability can also provide useful clues.

The difference between the short and long term variation of a process can provide clues as to the type of process improvements that may be required:

- **A large difference** indicates that the process performance could be improved through **better control**. The process **can** perform well but it is just not maintaining that performance. In this case, the process can be said to have **potential** if the control of it can be improved.

- **A small difference** indicates the process is already being controlled well over the longer term. So, if you still need better performance, it is unlikely to be available through improved control. In this case, the process can be said to be at the **limit of its potential** – the '**technology**' of the process can provide no more. This might suggest the project will involve re-designing the product or process.

So what is 'short' and 'long' term in real life:

Unfortunately the answer is once again 'it depends'. What may count as special cause variation when analysing short term data, might become viewed as common cause variation in light of the longer term data. It might be that your process has several levels of timescales: short term being just a few minutes, medium term being shift to shift, and long term might be season to season.

> ❗ Next time you are considering a major investment, make sure you are getting the most out of the existing one! A new machine or IT system can be an expensive solution to poor process control.

Process Capability – Introduction

Process capability is the assessment of how well the process delivers what the customer wants.

What is Process Capability?

Process Capability refers to a range of KPIs (metrics) that measure the ability of a process to deliver the customer's requirements. There are many alternative metrics explored on the next few pages and Six Sigma introduces a new Process Capability measure – the Sigma Level – described on page 85.

An example: The histogram opposite shows the delivery times of a home delivery service. The actual time of delivery is measured from the target delivery time (agreed with the customer) and so delivering perfectly on time would be measured as zero.

The range between the lower and upper specification limits is referred to as the **"Voice of the Customer"** (VOC). In this example the VOC is 2 hours – one hour either side of the target delivery time.

The total variation in the process (the width of the histogram) is referred to as the **"Voice of the Process"** (VOP) which, in a Normally distributed process such as the one shown here, is equivalent to 6 standard deviations.

> **❗ Specifications are not always the VOC!**
> Be careful not to assume that internal targets, specifications or manufacturing tolerances will reflect the customer's requirements.

Delivery Times from Target (decimal hours)

How do you *do* process capability?

Process capability is the comparison of the VOP to the VOC (process versus customer). In this case, since the width of the histogram (VOP) is smaller than the gap between the specification limits (VOC), it appears that this process should be capable of delivering within specifications. However, the histogram is not positioned centrally between the specification limits, meaning that deliveries tend to get delivered after the target time, and therefore there is a risk that some will be outside of the upper specification limit.

Both the **width** and **position** of the histogram define the capability of the process, and these characteristics are explored further on page 81.

Process Capability Routemap

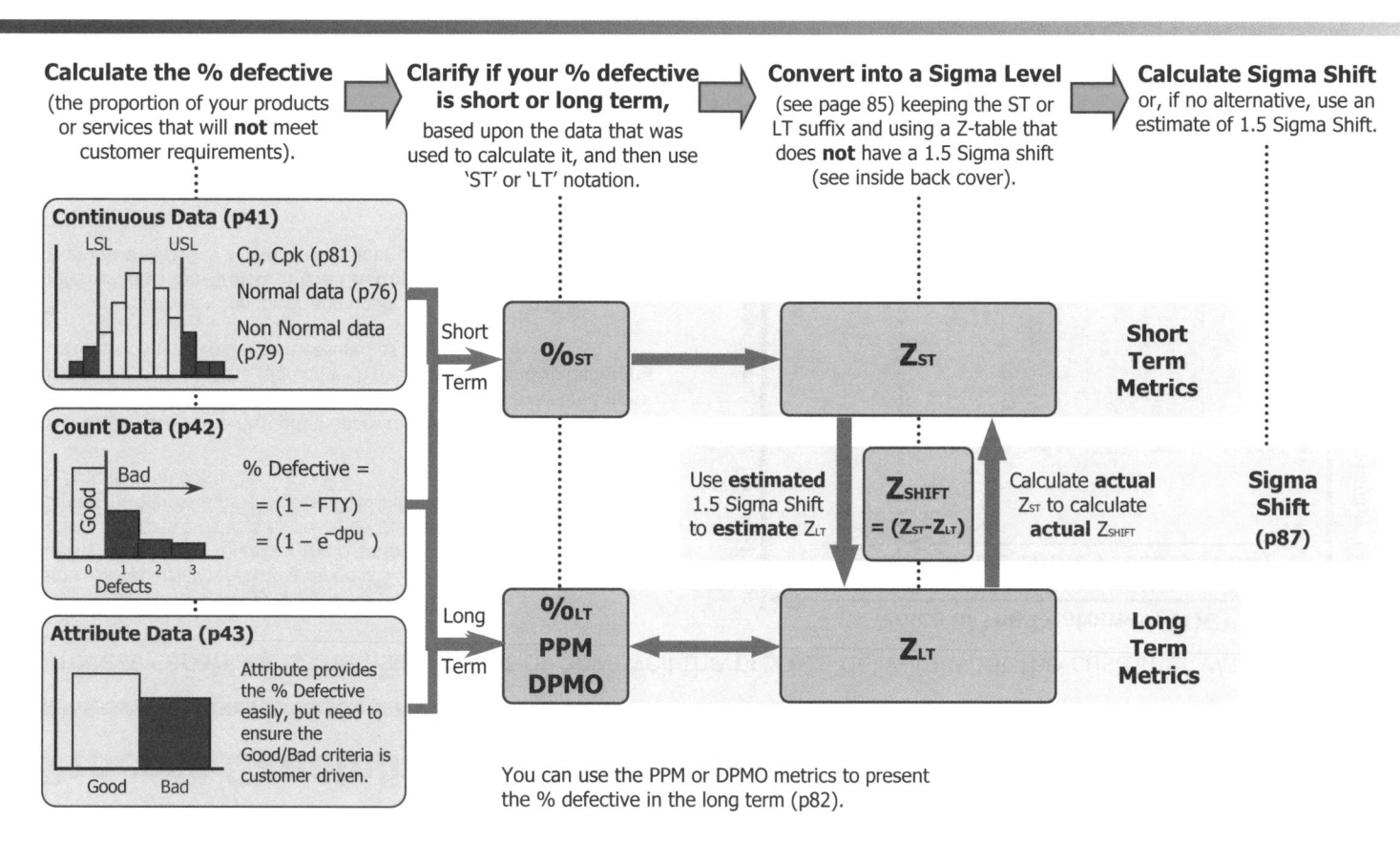

Calculate the % defective (the proportion of your products or services that will **not** meet customer requirements).

Clarify if your % defective is short or long term, based upon the data that was used to calculate it, and then use 'ST' or 'LT' notation.

Convert into a Sigma Level (see page 85) keeping the ST or LT suffix and using a Z-table that does **not** have a 1.5 Sigma shift (see inside back cover).

Calculate Sigma Shift or, if no alternative, use an estimate of 1.5 Sigma Shift.

Continuous Data (p41)

LSL   USL

Cp, Cpk (p81)

Normal data (p76)

Non Normal data (p79)

Count Data (p42)

Good   Bad

% Defective =
= $(1 - FTY)$
= $(1 - e^{-dpu})$

0 1 2 3
Defects

Attribute Data (p43)

Good   Bad

Attribute provides the % Defective easily, but need to ensure the Good/Bad criteria is customer driven.

Short Term

Long Term

$\%_{ST}$

$\%_{LT}$
PPM
DPMO

Z_{ST}

Short Term Metrics

Use **estimated** 1.5 Sigma Shift to **estimate** Z_{LT}

Z_{SHIFT}
$= (Z_{ST} - Z_{LT})$

Calculate **actual** Z_{ST} to calculate **actual** Z_{SHIFT}

Sigma Shift (p87)

Z_{LT}

Long Term Metrics

You can use the PPM or DPMO metrics to present the % defective in the long term (p82).

Minitab's Capability Analysis Functions

Minitab's capability analysis functions bring together many of the concepts introduced during measure such as histograms, distribution curves, short and long term variation.

Minitab: Stat > Quality Tools > Capability Analysis

(In version 13, theses functions are listed directly under Quality Tools)

The middle two functions provide similar analysis, but with multiple variables at the same time for comparison purposes. They are not explored further in this text.

The lower two functions are for use with Count data (Poisson) and Attribute data (Binomial). They are more advanced techniques and are not dealt with in detail in this text.

See page 84 for an approach to process capability with Count data and Attribute data.

The first three capability functions are for use with Continuous data.

The '**Normal**' method (p76) is obviously for data that is Normally distributed. It allows for natural subgroups within the data if necessary, but can also cope with a subgroup size of 1 (i.e. no natural subgroups).

The '**Between/Within**' method is very similar to the Normal method. It is used for data that was collected in very specific subgroups, but you will not make a mistake by opting for the "Normal" method if in doubt.

The '**Non-normal**' method (p79) should be used when your data is **clearly** skewed or Non-normal in any way. However it is more complex and should only be used once you are familiar with 'Normal' capability analysis. Versions 14 and 15 allows several alternative distributions to be specified, where as version 13 offers only Weibull.

Conducting Capability Studies: Capability studies can be conducted on historical data or data that was collected specifically for the purpose. In either case, it is important to ensure the data is recorded in time order, since Minitab will make this assumption.

In addition, and if possible, both the short and long term performance of the process should be reflected in the data you collect. A common approach is to collect small samples (subgroups) of say 5 or so measurements to reflect the short term, and to repeat this sampling at various intervals to capture the longer term variation in the process.

Capability Analysis with 'Normal' data – Input

A project is looking at the time it takes field teams to repair faults in air conditioning systems on customer sites. 5 (consecutive) repair tasks were sampled randomly every day for 20 days (so the data clearly has natural subgroups within it).

Use this option if your data is stacked in one column.

Use this option if your data is across several columns, with a row for each subgroup. (Enter all the columns that contain the data.)

Subgroups:

If the subgroup numbers are recorded in a column – enter that column here.

Note that the subgroups sizes do not need to be equal.

If the subgroups sizes **are** equal, then you can type the subgroup size direct into here.

If there are no subgroups, enter "1".

The data file contains two different versions of the same data to show the alternative methods of recording subgrouped data in Minitab.

  "Capability-RepairTimes.mpj"

Minitab: Stat > Quality Tools > Capability Analysis > Normal

If your data is not Normal, but can be transformed into Normal data using the **Box Cox** method (appendix G), then use this option.

The **Estimate** options define how the short term variation (within the subgroups) will be calculated. Check 'pooled standard deviation' and 'Average moving range' as a default.

The **Options** allow you to select the type of metrics that will be calculated. Choose between:
 - Parts per million or Percents (see p82)
 - Cp/Cpks or Sigma Levels (see p81/85)

Use **Storage** if you want the outputs to be stored in your worksheet in addition to the graphical output.

Enter the **customer's specifications** here. If the process only has one specification, leave the other blank. Tick the Boundary boxes if a specification represents a limit that it is impossible for the process to go beyond.

For this example, 6 hours is the maximum allowable by the customer, whist repairs taking less than 3 hours is an internal specification indicating over-resource.

Capability Analysis with 'Normal' data – Output

The specifications and statistics of the capability are summarised here.

Standard deviations:
The **'within'** value represents the short term variation of the process.
The **'overall'** value represents the long term.

Observed performance is based on the actual results used for the analysis. In this case no repairs took less than 3 hours, but 11 (out of 100) took longer than 6 hours. This 11% is equivalent to 110,000 parts per million.

The capability metrics given may be in Cp/Cpk (p81) or Sigma Level (p85) format depending on the Options selected.

The **Potential Capability** metrics are based on the short term variation. These reflect how good the process **could** be.

The **Overall Capability** metrics are based on all the variation seen in the analysis – the long term – and therefore reflect more truthfully the current performance of the process.

The long term metrics are called 'Pp' etc. to differentiate from their short term equivalents.

Process Capability of Time to fix fault (decimal hrs)

LSL = 3   USL = 6

Process Data	
LSL	3
Target	*
USL	6
Sample Mean	5.0333
Sample N	100
StDev (Within)	0.433805
StDev (Overall)	0.770317

Within
Overall

Potential (Within) Capability	
Cp	1.15
CPL	1.56
CPU	0.74
Cpk	0.74

Overall Capability	
Pp	0.65
PPL	0.88
PPU	0.42
Ppk	0.42
Cpm	*

3.0 3.5 4.0 4.5 5.0 5.5 6.0 6.5

Observed Performance		Exp. Within Performance		Exp. Overall Performance	
PPM < LSL	0.00	PPM < LSL	1.39	PPM < LSL	4150.65
PPM > USL	110000.00	PPM > USL	12926.18	PPM > USL	104750.60
PPM Total	110000.00	PPM Total	12927.56	PPM Total	108901.24

Expected Performance statistics are **predictions** of the proportions that will fail the specification limits. They are based on the areas under the Normal curves rather than the actual data in the histogram.

Two different sets are produced, one based on the short term performance (within) and one on the long term (overall).

Normal curves: In this example, the analysis found a large difference between the short term variation (standard deviation = 0.43) and the long term variation (standard deviation = 0.77).

The two Normal curves reflect this difference – the dashed line represents the long term, and the solid line represents the short term (it is much narrower/taller).

Capability Analysis with 'Non-Normal' data – Input

A project is looking at the amount of time that mortgage applications spend queuing between two critical steps in the application process.

The queue times of 100 mortgage applications are sampled from the process over a two month period (so both long and short term data can be assumed to be reasonably represented).

For operational reasons, the maximum acceptable queue time is 5 (working) hours, and the project leader wants to understand the capability of the process to meet this specification.

A histogram of the data indicates that the process distribution is skewed, and a Normality Test also indicates that the data is not Normally distributed.

Minitab's **Non-Normal** Capability analysis function is therefore appropriate, but it requires you to select an appropriate distribution to your date.

The Individual Distribution Identification function (see example on page 161) indicates that this data fits a Weibull distribution.

Minitab: Stat > Quality Tools > Capability Analysis > Nonnormal

Capability Analysis (Nonnormal Distribution)

| C1 | Queue Times |

Data are arranged as
- Single column: 'Queue Times'
- Subgroups across rows of:

Fit data with
- Distribution: Weibull
- Johnson transformation

Lower spec:
Upper spec: 5   ☐ Boundary

Estimate...
Options...
Storage...

Select
Help
OK
Cancel

For this example, leave the **Estimate** options as their default values.

The **Options** allow you to select the type of metrics that will be calculated. Choose between:
- Parts per million or Percents (see p82)
- Cp/Cpks or Sigma Levels (see p81/85)

Use **Storage** if you want the outputs to be stored in your worksheet in addition to the graphical output.

Enter the column containing your sampled process data here.

Select the distribution that fits your data from the drop down list.

Enter the specification limits of the process here. (In this case, there is only an upper specification).

💾 **"Capability-QueueTimes.mpj"**

Capability Analysis with 'Non-Normal' data – Output

The specifications and statistics of the capability are summarised here.

Observed performance statistics are based on the **actual** results within the data sample used for the analysis.

So, in this case, 2 of the 100 mortgage applications queued for more than five working hours and so the observed performance that exceeds the upper specification limit (USL) is 20,000 PPM (2%).

Because there was no lower specification limit (LSL), Minitab provides just an asterisk for 'PPM<LSL'.

Process Capability of Queue Times
Calculations Based on Weibull Distribution Model

Process Data	
LSL	*
Target	*
USL	5
Sample Mean	1.99499
Sample N	100
Shape	1.69368
Scale	2.23732

Observed Performance	
PPM < LSL	*
PPM > USL	20000.00
PPM Total	20000.00

Overall Capability	
Pp	*
PPL	*
PPU	0.64
Ppk	0.64

Exp. Overall Performance	
PPM < LSL	*
PPM > USL	20162.01
PPM Total	20162.01

The Pp and PPL statistics are blank because there is no lower specification limit in this example.

Ppk is similar to the Cpk statistic described on the next page, and a value of 0.64 indicates that this process is **not** a 'capable' for the longer term.

In this case, the expected performance figures predict that 20,162 parts per million will be above the USL if the process continues as it is.

20,162 PPM is the same as 20.1%.

Weibull curve: In this example, we asked Minitab to fit a Weibull distribution to the data. The Weibull curve shown here appears to fit the shape of the histogram reasonably well (as predicted by the Individual Distribution Identification function on page 161) and so we can assume that the expected performance figures (described opposite) will be reasonably reliable.

Expected Performance statistics are **predictions** of the proportions that will fail the specification limits. They are based on the areas under the fitted curves (in this case the Weibull distribution) rather than the actual data in the histogram and so can be a more reliable prediction (if the fitted model is suitable).

Process Capability – Cp and Cpk measures

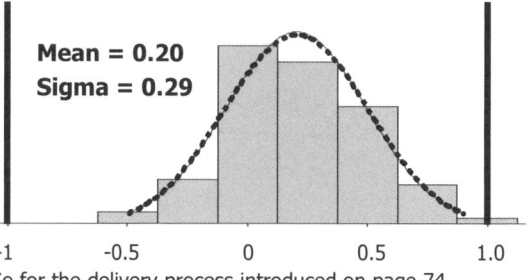

Mean = 0.20
Sigma = 0.29

-1   -0.5   0   0.5   1.0

So for the delivery process introduced on page 74 and re-shown above:

Cp = (1 - (-1)) / (6 * 0.29) = 1.39

Cpk = (1 - 0.2) / (3 * 0.29) = 0.92

Cp values of 1.33 or above are considered acceptable and a Cp above 2 is excellent (since it indicates that the specification window is twice as wide as the process variation).

The Cp of 1.39 indicates the delivery process is **capable** of providing the customers requirements, but the lower Cpk of 0.92 indicates that the process is not always **actually** meeting the customers requirements. This is because the process histogram is not positioned centrally between the specification limits.

 "Capability-DeliveryTimes.mpj"

The Cp metric reflects the *potential* capability of the process assuming that the histogram is positioned centrally within the speciation limits (VOC). Cp is therefore a ratio, and is defined as

$$Cp = \frac{\text{Voice of the Customer}}{\text{Voice of the Process}} = \frac{\text{width of the specification}}{\text{width of the histogram}} = \frac{(USL - LSL)}{6 * Sigma}$$

The Cpk metric reflects the *actual* capability of the process by measuring the same ratio as the Cp, but only to the nearest specification limit, since this is the limit which is most likely to be failed. Cpk is defined as:

$$Cpk = \frac{\text{Nearest Voice of the Customer}}{\text{Half of Voice of the Process}} = \frac{(\text{Nearest spec.} - \text{Process Average})}{3 * Sigma}$$

Poor capability, but centred
Cp = 0.9
Cpk = 0.9

Poor capability, and not centred
Cp =0.9
Cpk = 0.5

Good capability, and centred
Cp = 2.0
Cpk = 2.0

Good capability, but not centred
Cp = 2.0
Cpk = - 0.5

Process Capability – PPM and DPMO measures

'Per Opportunity' – Process capability metrics that contain the phrase 'per opportunity' are used to account for the level of complexity in a process when assessing its capability. They work by dividing the number of failures in a process by the number of opportunities for things to go wrong (complexity).

So, a highly complex process that is producing 5% scrap would have a better (lower) failure rate "per opportunity" than a less complex process running at the same 5% scrap.

This seems reasonable but in reality the use of "per opportunity" measures has proven to be far from practical, because of the difficulty in measuring complexity.

So how do you measure complexity?

Most approaches to measuring complexity do so by counting the number of *opportunities for defects* (OFDs) in a product and process. The counting of OFDs usually involves counting factors such as the number of process steps, parts, connections or handovers in a process, but this is not dealt with in any more depth within this text.

Whichever approach is used, the key success factor is that it must be applied **consistently.** There is little value in comparing **per opportunity** metrics if the basis for counting OFDs is inconsistent!

Whilst the use of complexity measures can be difficult for process capability purposes, it does have an important role in the (re)design of processes and products, i.e: Design for Six Sigma (DFSS).

A focus on complexity should be the corner stone of every Business Process Re-engineering (BPR) project or new product design. For this reason, measuring complexity is often more relevant within the Improve phase of most projects.

'Per Million' – Process capability metrics that contain the phrase 'per million' are used to expand the scale so that smaller differences become more measurable. This may not seem relevant to your processes at this stage but as process capability improves, so will the resolution you require to measure it. With this approach, a 0.2% scrap rate becomes expressed as 2000 scrap parts *per million* – a much more challenging target to reduce!

An everyday example of this type of metric is chemical dilution rates (such as the amount of chlorine in a swimming pool). Because these rates are low, they are sometimes quoted as 'parts per million'.

PPM – Parts per million: As discussed, this metric can be used to 'amplify' a percentage and is often used to convey how many defective products or services will be delivered over the longer term.

DPMO – Defects per million opportunities: This metric incorporates both the *per million* and *per opportunity* concepts and is often proposed as a key Six Sigma metric. In reality, we would recommend avoiding DPMO unless the pitfalls of complexity measurement can be reliably overcome.

Only use long term data to calculate PPM and DPMO rates!
PPM and DPMO are both aimed at describing the defect rate over the longer term (several million). For this reason, you should not take a % defective rate that is based upon short term data and magnify it into a PPM or DPMO metric. Your long term prediction would inevitably be over optimistic, since actual performance over the longer term is almost always worse than the short term.

Calculating '% Defective' for Continuous Data

Calculating the overall % Defective is the key output from a Capability Analysis

Calculating the total % Defective: As shown in the graph opposite, the total % Defective is calculated by adding the % Defectives falling outside of each specification limit together.

The % Defectives that fall outside each specification limit are calculated using the Z-table as described below, or using Minitab (below right).

Continuing the CD thickness example from page 70, suppose a lower specification limit (LSL) of 1.25mm was required by the customer, in addition to the existing upper limit of 1.5mm.

The histogram opposite shows clearly that some CDs will fail the LSL, and we already know a small number (0.6%) will fail the USL (p70).

We also know that: Average CD thickness = 1.35mm (rounded)
Standard Deviation of CD thickness = 0.06mm

- The USL is 2.5 Sigma away from the average ((1.5 - 1.35) / 0.06), and the Z-table predicts that 0.6% of CDs will be too thick (above USL).

- The LSL is 1.65 Sigma away from the average ((1.35 - 1.25) / 0.06) and the Z-table predicts that 4.95% of CDs will be too thin (below the LSL).

So, the total % Defective CDs will be (0.6 + 4.95) = 5.55%

Short term or Long term? Don't forget to add a short term or long term code to this % Defective. From page 70, we can find that the data is based upon a small sample of just 100 CDs, and so we should add the code ST (short term) to this % Defective figure, to remind us that it may not represent how the process will perform in the longer term.

The % defectives from each specification are combined to make a total % Defective rate of 5.55%

Using Minitab to calculate the total % Defective:

The **Expected Overall Performance** figures in either the Normal or Non-normal versions of Minitab's capability analysis function will provide the total % Defective figure discussed here. The figure will be quoted as **PPM Total** or **% Total** depending on the options selected.

Exp. Overall Performance	
PPM < LSL	50786.71
PPM > USL	6221.17
PPM Total	57007.88

Calculating '% Defective' for Count and Attribute Data

% Defective in the Count data world: If you are counting **defects** then by definition, the products or services which are 'good' are those that have **no** defects. For example, the histogram below shows the number of scratches found on 100 mobile phone screens when they reached the customer. The majority (58) of the phones had **no** scratches, but some had one or more scratches. So, the % Defective is the proportion of phones that had **one or more** scratches, as follows:

$$\% \text{ Defective} = \frac{\text{No. of phones with 1 or more scratches}}{\text{Total number of phones}}$$

In this case, the % Defective was 42%, since 42 phones had **one or more** scratches out of the 100.

% Defective for Attribute data:

Attribute data is already divided into 'good' and 'bad' results, and therefore the % Defective is simply just the % of 'bad' results from the sample.

For example, out of a sample of 100 computers, 79 passed and 21 failed the final test before shipment, and so the % Defective is 21%. As always, this should be quoted with a short term or long term code (since only 100 computers were tested, this example would be likely to be short term).

Alternative approach to calculating the % Defective with Count data:

Defects per unit (DPU) is the key statistic of the Count data world (page 42) and it represents the average number of defects found on each unit. It would seem rational that there is a relationship between DPU and the % Defective, since a **high DPU** (lots of defects) would mean a **high % Defective rate.** The mathematical relationship shown below can be used to calculate the % Defective from the average DPU. This approach provides a better estimate of the % Defective since it utilises the Poisson model that lies behind Count data.

$$\text{FTY} = e^{-DPU} * 100\% \quad \text{OR} \quad \% \text{ Defective} = (1 - e^{-DPU}) * 100\%$$

So, for the mobile phone example:

The DPU is 0.59 (average scratches / phone) which is calculated as follows: 28 phones had 1 scratch, 11 phones had 2 scratches, 3 phones had 3 scratches – making a total of 59 scratches on 100 phones (0.59 per phone).

With a DPU of 0.59, the equation shown on the left provides % Defective of 44.6%.

This is slightly higher, and more reliable, than the 42% produced directly from the raw data.

Process Capability – Sigma Levels

With so many different process capability metrics available, Six Sigma aimed to create one common metric that would apply to all data worlds and environments – the Sigma Level (or Sigma Value).

Sigma Levels in Theory:

As can be seen on the previous pages, there are numerous metrics used for quantifying Process Capability and many more that are company or industry specific.   Six Sigma aims to bring them all together through a common 'Sigma Level' metric.

Two key advantages of Sigma Levels are:

- they are a common capability measure that allows processes to be benchmarked against each other across different industries, technologies, data worlds etc.

- their scale is not linear. Sigma levels have increasing resolution at low defect levels, allowing the difference between 99.8% and 99.9% (for example) to be reflected in a more significant way.

Sigma Levels in Practice:

It's a nice idea, but unfortunately there is already a universal measure of process capability – the percentage!   The percentage is something that is so common place and well understood that it is difficult to envisage a complete transition to Sigma Levels.

However, having said that, this book would not be complete without providing an understanding of how Sigma Levels work, so that the reader can converse in either format!

What is a Sigma level?

The Sigma level is the same as the Z value in the Z-table.

Imagine a Normally distributed process that only has an upper specification limit (USL), as shown below.   Its Sigma level is defined as the distance between the average and the USL, in units of standard deviations (i.e its Z value).

Area = % Defective

To work out the Sigma level for any process, you must equate it to this Normally distributed process, with just an upper specification limit.

It can be seen from the diagram above, that as the process moves further away from the specification limit (to the left), the Sigma Level (Z) will increase, and the proportion of products falling outside the USL (the % Defective) will reduce.

So, a higher Sigma Level equates to higher performance and vice versa.

Process Capability – Sigma Levels (cont.)

Regardless of the environment or the data world, Sigma Levels are calculated by equating every process to the 'imaginary' (one sided) process defined in the Z-table.

As explained on the previous page, the Z-table is also a table of Sigma Levels, and can be used to translate the % Defective of a process into a Sigma Level, and vice versa.

- So, if you know the % Defective of your process (either as a proportion, percentage, PPM or DPMO), then you can use the Z-table to convert this into a Sigma Level.

- Alternatively, if someone tells you that a process is running at a performance (Sigma) level of 2 Sigma, then you can use the Z-table to convert this into a % Defective of 2.3%.

The Z-table is therefore really a conversion table between two different scales – the % Defective and Sigma Levels. The (very) abbreviated table below shows some key Sigma Levels to remember, and a fuller version can be found inside the back cover of this text.

% Defective	Sigma Level
50 %	0.0
31 %	0.5
16 %	1.0
7 %	1.5
2.3 %	2.0
0.6 %	2.5
0.13 %	3.0

Sigma Level examples from previous pages...

Continuous Data World example on page 83

For the CD thickness example, the total % Defective was calculated to be 5.55% (or thereabouts allowing for rounding).
So, from the Z-table, this equates to a Sigma Level of 1.60 Sigma.

Count Data World example on page 84

For the example about scratches on mobile phone screens, the total % Defective was calculated to be 44.6% (from the alternative method using DPU).
So, from the Z-table, this equates to a Sigma Level of 0.15 Sigma.

Attribute Data World example on page 84

For the example on the final testing of computers, the total % Defective at final test was 21%.
So, from the Z-table, this equates to a Sigma Level of 0.8 Sigma.

Note that some of the above Sigma Levels have been rounded slightly from the Z-table.

Process Capability – Sigma Shift

The difference between short and long term performance needs to be reflected in Sigma Levels

Page 73 describes the significant differences in performance that can occur between the short and long(er) term. This is shown graphically in the time series plot opposite, but has not been considered so far during the range of process capability measures described over the last few pages. Whilst summarising process performance, it is important to be aware of whether the data being used represents the process over the short or long term.

Minitab's Capability Analysis uses a statistical approach to identifying short term and longer term variation within a data set. It separates the capability of the process in the short term (for which it uses Cp and Cpk) from that of the long term (using Pp and Ppk metrics). A detailed example can be found on page 76.

Sigma Shift in Theory: Sigma Levels based on long term data are generally lower than those calculated from short term data. The difference between them is called **Sigma Shift**.

Based on empirical evidence, a typical 'Sigma Shift' between the short and long term is around 1.5.

This means that difference between short and long term performance is caused by the process average 'wandering' by up to +/- 1.5 Sigma.

Sigma Levels were originally intended only to be used to represent the capability of a process in the short term.

Sigma Shift in Practice: In reality, Sigma Shift is different for every process and its measurement is important to understanding how the process might be improved. So, the generic application of 1.5

Sigma Shift should be only be used as a last resort, to estimate the difference between the short and long terms.

In addition, Sigma Levels tend to be used for Long and Short term data, with no distinction between them, causing significant confusion!

A practical approach to using Sigma Levels:

▪ If at all possible, collect long term data from your process, and calculate the **actual** Sigma Shift of your process (see next page).

▪ Always add a suffix code to your capability metrics, including Sigma Levels, to indicate whether they represent the short term (Z_{ST}) or the long term (Z_{LT}).

So why does my Z-table look different!?

The use of a generic 1.5 Sigma Shift causes a significant amount of confusion, and it is fair to say that this situation is perpetuated by 'experts' who continue to confuse and baffle their trainees with it during Six Sigma training!   For example:

▪ You will hear people refer to a Six Sigma process as delivering 3.4 DPMO, when what they actually mean is that a process that is Six Sigma **in the short term,** will be 4.5 Sigma **in the long term,** and **that is** equivalent to 3.4 DPMO.

▪ In addition, some Z-tables and Sigma Level tables have been pre-adjusted to include the 1.5 Sigma Shift, whether you like it or not!

How confusing!   So how to get around this problem?

1) Avoid Z-Tables that have the 1.5 Sigma Shift built into them. It is easy to make the wrong prediction with these tables.

2) Use the routemap through Sigma Shift described opposite, and always keep your Sigma Levels labelled as either short or long term.

3) Do not estimate Sigma Shift to be 1.5!   Using the generic 1.5 Sigma Shift misses the whole point (and as many statisticians will tell you, is highly dubious in its validity).   Instead, you should always try and collect **real** data from your process that represents the **real** Sigma Shift of your process.   Sigma Shift represents the difference between the short and long term variation of your process - see p73.

💾 **"Z-Table & Sigma Levels.xls"**

A Routemap through Sigma Shift

I have collected long term data...

▪ You can work out the long term Sigma Level and label it Z_{LT}.

▪ You can also convert your long term data into PPM or DPMO metrics, since these are for use with long term data.

...and now I want to work out the short term performance of the process, to see how good the process could be:

▪ You can find the short term performance of your process from **within** your long term data (Minitab process capability can do this for you).

▪ You can then convert the short term performance into a Sigma Level, and work out your Sigma Shift ($Z_{ST} - Z_{LT}$)

I have collected only short term data...

▪ You can work out your short term Sigma Level, but make sure you label it Z_{ST}, so that people know it represents the short term only.

▪ *Do not* multiply your short term proportions into PPM or DPMO figures, since these are for long term data only.

...and now I want to work out what the long term performance of my process will be:

▪ Unless you can continue collecting real data over the long term (the ideal option), you can only estimate what Z_{LT} will be!

▪ If you really have to estimate it, then you can subtract 1.5 from your short term Sigma Level to **estimate** a long term Sigma Level (Z_{LT}). Be careful with this long term estimate! Make sure you keep it clearly labeled as an estimate. Your process might actually turn out to be better or worse in the long term – time will tell!

Measure – Checklist

❑ Have relevant Key Performance Indicators (KPIs) been selected and/or developed?

❑ Have the KPIs been defined clearly using process maps or diagrams and operational definitions?

❑ Is there a data collection plan in place for the KPIs, including sampling where appropriate?

❑ Is relevant contextual information being collected alongside the KPIs? (for stratification of the data during Analyse)

❑ Has the quality of the data been checked/challenged using Measurement System Analysis (GR&R etc.) techniques.

❑ Has a '1st Pass Analysis' (Histograms and Time Series plots) of the KPIs been completed using the historical data?

❑ Has the type of variation in the process (common cause or special cause) been considered?

❑ Has the difference between the short and long term performance of the process been considered?

❑ Have valid KPI baselines been set based on the historical data?

❑ Have defect definitions and specification limits been developed that are relevant to the Voice of Customer?

❑ Has the process capability been analysed, and the problem and goal statement updated if necessary?

❑ Has a Sigma Level been calculated? (if your organisation uses this capability measure).

Measure – Review Questions

▪ What KPIs have been selected for the problem?   Why?

▪ What data worlds do the KPIs come from (continuous/count/attribute)?

▪ Where is the data for the KPIs coming from?

▪ Was the data already available, or did you have to introduce more data collection?   If so, is it temporary for the project, or permanent?

▪ Is 100% of the process being measured, or is it being sampled?

▪ If sampling – what is the sampling strategy and why?

▪ What other contextual information is being collected with KPIs.

▪ How was the quality of the data checked? (does it represent what it is supposed to represent)?

▪ What has been learnt about the historical behaviour of the process?

▪ Does the process look stable (statistically in control) or unstable?

▪ What is the best the process has ever performed?   And worst?

▪ Over what time period was the baseline performance of the process established?

▪ How was the Voice of the Customer reflected when establishing the capability of the process?

▪ Has the process capability been converted into a Sigma Level?

Overview of Analyse

The Analyse phase aims to identify critical factors of a 'good' product or service, and the root causes of 'defects'.   It has less of a logical flow, but functions more as a toolbox of tools and techniques.

The flow through Analyse:

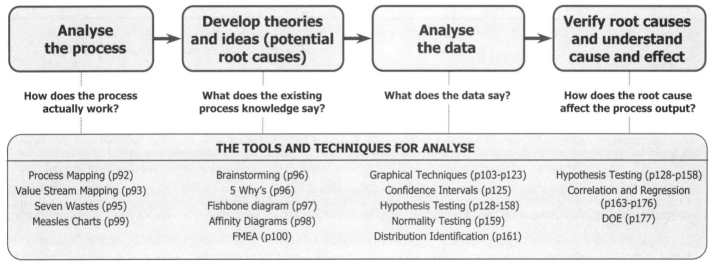

Analyse the process	Develop theories and ideas (potential root causes)	Analyse the data	Verify root causes and understand cause and effect
How does the process actually work?	What does the existing process knowledge say?	What does the data say?	How does the root cause affect the process output?

THE TOOLS AND TECHNIQUES FOR ANALYSE

Process Mapping (p92)	Brainstorming (p96)	Graphical Techniques (p103-p123)	Hypothesis Testing (p128-p158)
Value Stream Mapping (p93)	5 Why's (p96)	Confidence Intervals (p125)	Correlation and Regression (p163-p176)
Seven Wastes (p95)	Fishbone diagram (p97)	Hypothesis Testing (p128-158)	DOE (p177)
Measles Charts (p99)	Affinity Diagrams (p98)	Normality Testing (p159)	
	FMEA (p100)	Distribution Identification (p161)	

The Process Door Routemap (page 91):   The first two steps of Analyse are also referred to as the 'Process Door' because they aim to understand and gain clues directly from the process itself. The tools focus on gaining an in-depth understanding of how the process really works, and so most of them involve the people who know the process best – those who 'make it happen'.

The Data Door Routemap (page 102):   The last two steps are also referred to as the 'Data Door' because they focus on gaining clues and understanding from the data itself. These tools include a range of graphical and statistical tools to analyse the data.

The 'Process Door' – Finding The Right Tool

Process Mapping is a common starting point for the 'process door' – mapping the **real** process. The remainder of the Process Door tools focus on analysing when, where, and how, the process might fail.

Getting to know the process: The first stage of Analyse involves getting out of the office and going to see the process.   Regardless of the type of product or service involved, there is no substitute for gaining an intimate understanding of the process at this stage. Process mapping helps, but before that it should be something even more practical... ***go do the process, provide the service or make the product!!!***

In the **manufacturing** world, engineers and designers should spend time operating the machines and products they design.

The same principles apply to the **transactional** environment...   spend a shift or two answering the calls or filling out purchase requisitions, go out with a service technician for a day, or spend a week on the reception desk of your hotel, and you will soon notice things you never knew before.

The boxes below will help you find the appropriate 'Process Door' technique to use based on what it is you need to know.

Getting to know the process as it actually happens in reality...
- Process Mapping (p92) & The Seven Wastes (p95)
- Value Stream Mapping (p93) & Time Value Maps (p94)

Investigate a failure to understand its root cause...
- 5 Whys (p96)

Assessing what *could* go wrong and where...
- Failure Mode and Effects Analysis (FMEA) (p100)

Understanding what *does* go wrong in the process and where...
- Affinity Diagrams (p98)
- Measles Charts (p99)

Identifying possible root causes...
- Brainstorming (p96)

Structure the possible root causes in a logical manner...
- Fishbone (Cause and Effect) Diagram (p97)

Process Mapping

The flowcharts contained in procedures and quality manuals show how the process *should* be. Process mapping is the detailed mapping of the *real* process.

Amongst other benefits, process maps help bring clarity to complex processes and to highlight non-value added processes (such as rework loops, sign-off's, redundant or repeated processes etc.)

Process maps are also used to record various types of **supplementary information,** depending on the focus of the project.

The example opposite focuses on rework loops, failure modes and failure rates, but other examples include; lead times, process ownership (geographical, organisational or contractual etc.), data collection points, First Time Yields, inventory levels, optional processes etc.

Rework loops: One of the most common purposes of process mapping is to help identify the rework loops in a process. Most processes have some formal, documented rework loops for recognised problems. This might be evident by finding complaint forms, stock adjustment forms, RMA (Return Merchandise Authorisation) forms etc. However, most processes also have an abundance of informal rework loops that can only be identified by asking 'what can go wrong' at every stage of the detailed process mapping.

Complexity to simplicity: Process maps become very complex very quickly, and you will soon find you have to re-write the map for clarity. A useful approach is to have different levels within the map, and to only detail a specific area of the process at any one time. The example above demonstrates this hierarchical approach; only the 'install service' level 1 process has been process mapped in level 2 detail.

Standard symbols help to ensure process maps are written in a consistent manner. There are a number of different standards, but processes are usually contained in squares and formal decision points such as inspection or testing in diamonds. It is worth checking whether your organisation has any standard symbols that you should comply with.

Value Stream Mapping (VSM)

Value Stream Mapping (VSM) is an advanced form of process mapping, which focuses on the process using the principles of Lean and from the perspective of Value.

This VSM example of a telecom equipment installation process shows a sample of the information that you might collect. VSM introduces lots of new symbols – some of which are shown on the next page.

Set Up Time	10 mins
Process Time	75 mins
Queue Time	3100 mins
# People	12

Set Up Time	1 mins
Process Time	10 mins
Queue Time	1500 mins
# People	2

Set Up Time	5 mins
Process Time	120 mins
Queue Time	0 mins
# People	30

The Value Steam Mapping Process:

- Gain clear scope for the VSM
- Document the **as is** process flow, focusing on material and data flows
- Collect additional data (as required by your project focus)
- Gain consensus from the process owners and your project team

Lean focused data that is useful to collect:

- Queue Times / Set up times / Process Times / Transport Times
- Inventory (In Queue / In transport / In process)
- Number of people / machines
- Batch Sizes
- Defect Rates
- Existence of Kanbans
- Sources of data

VSM Symbols

A selection of useful VSM symbols...

Customer or Supplier ----

A queue of 25 units of inventory --------------

Physical flow of parts -------

Flow of manual information (e.g. forms) --- Monthly

Flow of electronic information (e.g. EDI) ----------------- Daily

A potential improvement project -------

An electronic database -----

Number of employees ----------------------

Transport -----------

Time Value Map

A Time Value Map demonstrates graphically the proportion of time that is spent adding value.

A Time Value Map is constructed using the Queue and Process times recorded during Value Stream Mapping. In addition, each process step is classified into one of the following three categories:

Value Add Activities (VA - blue); increase the value of the product/service from the customer perspective.

Business Non-Value Add Activities (BNVA – light grey); are necessary for the business, but the customer would not be willing to pay extra for them (e.g. regulatory, data entry, invoicing, purchasing, research and development).

Non Value Add Activities (NVA – dark grey); add no value and are not required for business operational reasons either. This includes all of the seven wastes (see next page).

The Seven Wastes, plus some new ones

Taichi Ohno defined the Seven Wastes – a useful structure when eliminating and preventing waste. Several new wastes have subsequently been added, along with wastes specific to service industries.

The Seven Wastes:

▪ **Overproduction** – making more products than the customer requires. This waste increases WIP and lead times, hides poor quality rates, requires extra storage and promotes a batch and queue type approach.

▪ **Waiting** – any time that a product is waiting, lead times are increasing, and no value (the only thing a customer pays for) is being added.

▪ **Transporting** – moving things unnecessarily costs money, time and usually requires a return loop – all without adding value for the customer!

▪ **Over processing** – refers to adding more value (features and specifications) to the product or service than the customer will be pay for. Inappropriate processing is slightly different, and refers to the use of inappropriate equipment that is over engineered for the purpose, and therefore adds more cost than value.

▪ **Unnecessary Inventory** – holding and creating excessive inventory costs money and increases lead times. Some inventory is necessary, but most processes can be managed differently to minimise inventory.

▪ **Unnecessary Motion** – needles movements at an ergonomic level have a significant effect on overall efficiency, and are also increasingly the source of health and safety issues.

▪ **Defects (or errors)** – the clearest waste of all, defects and mistakes require fixing or replacing and have a direct effect on the bottom line.

Some new wastes:

▪ **Wasted human potential** – traditional hierarchical cultures waste significant skills and expertise in the workforce.

▪ **Wasted Energy** – the finite aspect of fossil fuels has raised awareness of wasting energy and increased its effect on the bottom line. This will increase further as global warming takes hold.

▪ **Pollution** – historically a hidden shared cost to us all, the producer is increasingly being made to pay for pollution, raising its importance.

▪ **Wasted Space** – the premium on space in certain environments is at an all time high, and its waste is therefore something the customer will not pay for.

Wastes from the service perspective:

▪ **Delay in provision** – time is an important element of the value of a service, and therefore can have a significant cost impact.

▪ **Incorrect inventory** – the wrong inventory (or being out of stock) is a significant waste in the service sector, where customers tend not to wait, and instead move on to another provider.

▪ **Duplication** – service processes rely heavily on the handling and processing of data, and frequently involve duplicated data entry or unnecessary transfer of data.

Brainstorming

5 Why's

Brainstorming can be used to consider a whole range of possible root causes to a *type of failure*.

As you may be aware, brainstorming is a valuable technique that can be used in many environments, for many purposes.

In Six Sigma projects, brainstorming is often used at the beginning of the Analyse phase. Whilst "5 Why's" can be used to investigate specific failures, brainstorming can be used to identify a range of potential root causes for a particular type of failure.

Brainstorming in practice:

A brainstorming session needs careful **facilitation.** If ideas are slow, then the facilitator can use "prompting questions" to help the group focus on a specific area for a while. If someone is feeling unable to participate, the facilitator needs to help them to do so.

The **team** should represent several levels of the organisation since this helps to capture the different impressions people have of the problem.

Different approaches to brainstorming:

Whilst running a session, participants can either be asked to give an idea each in turn (better for ensuring everyone feels able to participate but can be intimidating) or can be given a 'free-for all' (which requires more careful facilitation).

Alternatively, brainstorming can be done over time by placing a Fishbone diagram (see next page) on the wall for a week or two and inviting everyone to write their ideas on it.

'5 Why's' can be used to investigate a *specific failure* to find a problems real root cause.

If a problem is going to be fixed, the real root cause needs to be understood. Sometimes it is useful to randomly select 2-3 real failures in the process and to investigate them in much more detail, using '5 Why's' – a simple but effective technique.

5 Why's is a bit like being an inquisitive 4 year old who keeps asking why? You take a real failure and investigate by asking why, why, why…

Problem: **Parcel got lost in post**

Why?: Because it got stolen from the customer's front door.

Why?: Because the customer was not in to sign for it

Why?: Because the customer had gone out during the agreed delivery period.

Why: Because the customer had forgotten the delivery was due

Why: Because the delivery was arranged several weeks in advance, and the customer was not reminded.

Once the real root cause is understood, the chance of an effective solution is greatly improved. For example, the lead time between arrangement and delivery could be reduced or reminders could be send out (by e-mail/text/post) 2 days before delivery etc.

Be careful not to let your answers get too broad. If you always end up concluding that the root cause is "poor management" or "terrible suppliers" (even though they might be!) then it is not going to be specific enough to help solve the problem.

Fishbone (Cause and Effect) Diagrams

Fishbone diagrams are usually used during brainstorming sessions on root causes. However, they can be also be used throughout the Analyse phase as a great tool for structuring a team's thoughts.

Fishbone diagrams are an effective tool to help facilitate brainstorming sessions. The example shown here is the output of a brainstorming session on the causes of low fuel efficiency in a car.

Categories on Fishbone diagrams:

There are many different versions of Fishbone diagrams – with different branch names (people, methods etc). This is because there are no right or wrong ones; just use those that are appropriate to your application, or create your own.

Other uses of Fishbone diagrams:

As projects move into the Analyse phase, they usually start to have several different 'areas of investigation'. Although not technically being used for 'root causes' analysis, a fishbone diagram can provide clarity by being used to document the structure of the project, with each 'line of enquiry' represented by a 'branch'.

How to document a fishbone diagrams: The best way to start a fishbone is with a large piece of paper on the wall, or a white board – a pretty fishbone diagram is not your first objective! Afterwards you'll probably want to document your results. A blank template is available in the data file: **"Fishbone Template.ppt"**

Affinity Diagrams

Affinity Diagrams help to analyse the categories within textual data, such as the key types of failure in a product or service, or the key issues contained with customer feedback forms.

During the Measure phase, you may have implemented data collection forms that ask for the details of a failure to be written down.

During the Analyse phase, you will find lots of anecdotal evidence of failures within the system – particularly during process mapping.

Affinity diagrams are a technique for finding similar groups within these sorts of textual (non numeric) data.

How to construct an affinity diagram:

▪ Write each bit of textual data on a separate paper note, and lay them out on a table or a wall.

▪ Ask the project team to start moving the notes around so that ones that are similar are placed together. They should do this in silence, and not look to explain their thinking for moving a note – just do it! (other participants are allowed to move notes back again if they disagree).

▪ Once natural clusters have emerged in the notes, discuss them within the group and give each cluster a name. Some clusters may have only 1 or 2 notes.

What can be done with the output of affinity diagrams:

▪ Reason codes (for data collection forms) can be designed with more relevance.

▪ The largest clusters can be focussed on for problem solving during the Analyse phase.

Before...

After...

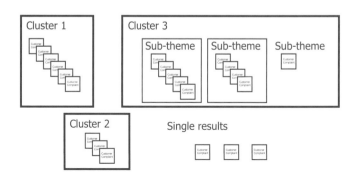

Measles Charts

Measles charts are a practical tool for collecting data that help to analyse the **location** of failures in a product or process.

Although you may be measuring the failure rate or 'First Time Yield' of a process, these will not necessarily tell you where most of the problems occur. Measles charts are a very visual and practical method of plotting the location and density of failures onto a symbolic drawing or picture of a product or process.

When to use Measles Charts:

They can be done alongside process mapping during Analyse, or used as part of a data collection plan during Measure.

Example: A can production process has excessive downtime due to parts jamming in the pressing machine. A picture of the press is set up on the shop floor and every time a can jams, the location of the jam is marked on the picture (Measles chart) with a red dot. After a short period of time, this helps to confirm that the biggest cause of jams is the lip of the can catching a specific part of the ejection mechanism.

Example: Car hire companies use Measles Charts to record car damage. When you deliver back a hire car, you are asked to note any damage to the car on a simple picture of the car.

Example: A project is looking at reducing the number of invoices that get returned from clients. A standard invoice is printed out as a poster, and placed on the wall of the office. For every returned invoice, a dot is placed on the invoice poster. This quickly highlights that the Delivery Address and the calculation of Tax are the most common problems.

Failure Mode and Effect Analysis (FMEA)

FMEA can be used during Analyse, Improve or Control to highlight the area of a product or process that should be targeted for improvement – without any failures having actually occurred.

Process Step or Product Part	Potential Failure Mode	Potential Failure Effects	S E V	Potential Causes	O C C	Current Controls	D E T	RPN	Actions Recommended	Who?	Actions Taken	S E V	O C C	D E T	RPN
Accept order	Wrong customer address	Missed delivery	5	Typo on postal code	3	Check street name with customer	4	60							0

What is an FMEA? An FMEA is essentially a risk analysis tool that can be useful in environments where you have to prevent an event ever happening (e.g. safety) or where the failure rate for a process is so low that there is little opportunity to learn from past failures.   There are two key types used within Six Sigma:

1) Product FMEAs analyse the function, design and potential failure of each component of a product.

2) Process FMEAs analyse the key outputs and potential failure of each step of a process, and consider the affect of process failure on the product or service concerned.

The FMEA process:

▪ Identify the process steps or components of the product.

▪ For each step/component, list the different failure modes that can occur and rate their **severity (SEV).**

▪ For each failure mode, consider the different potential causes that might cause the failure and rate their **occurrence (OCC)** – how likely they are to occur.

▪ For each potential cause, consider the controls in place to prevent it happening and/or to detect the failure if the cause does occur. Then rate the likelihood of **detection (DET)**.

▪ Calculate a Risk Priority Number (RPN) for each potential failure by multiplying the Severity by Occurrence by Detection.

▪ Act on the results!! Assign actions to tackle the highest RPN's, and set a date to review progress.

The FMEA structure above shows a typical format.

The left hand side (first nine columns) are completed during the first draft of the FMEA, and the right hand side (remaining seven columns) are used to track subsequent actions and document reduced RPNs.

FMEAs should be seen as living documents, not something that you do and store away in a filing cabinet somewhere. Having identified a risk, you must do something about it!

Failure Mode and Effect Analysis (FMEA)

Rating Severity, Occurrence and Detection:

The ratings for severity, occurrence and detection are usually on a scale of 1 to 10. There are several versions of tables that help to define the different ratings, as shown opposite. These are available in the FMEA template data file:

💾 **"FMEA Template & Ratings.xls"**

Applying ratings can create much discussion and debate. Be careful not to let your FMEA team waste time on deciding whether something should be rated a 2 instead of a 3! The most important thing is that you apply your rating scales consistently.

It is worth customising your tables to your organisation's environment. Using plain language helps people to relate to the definitions and to apply more consistent ratings.

FMEAs in practice:

As with many of the other tools in the 'Process Door', you need to assemble a team from across the process. Make sure you involve the people who 'do', manage and design the process.

FMEAs rapidly expand in size, as each process step (or part) can have several failure modes, which in turn have several potential causes, which can have several relevant controls. For this reason, they require careful facilitation in order to keep them on course and completed in time. You will need to plan for several sessions!

SEVERITY of Effects of Failure Mode

Effect	Criteria	Ranking
Hazardous - without warning	• Very high severity ranking when a potential failure mode affects safe product operation and /	10
Hazardous - with warning		
Very High		
High		
Moderate		
Low		
Very Low		
Minor		
Very Minor		
None		

OCCURRENCE of Failure Mode

Probability of Failure	Possible Failure	Ranking
Very High: Failure is almost inevitable		
High: Repeated failure		
Moderate: Occasional failures		
Low: Relatively few failures		
Remote: Failure is unlikely.		

DETECTION of the Failure Mode

Detection	Criteria	Ranking
Absolute Uncertainty	Design Control will not and / or can not detect a potential cause mechanism and subsequent failure mode; or there is no design control	10
Very Remote	Very remote chance the design control will detect a potential cause / mechanism and subsequent failure mode	9
Remote	Remote chance the design control will detect a potential cause / mechanism and subsequent failure mode	8
Very Low	Very low chance the design control will detect a potential cause / mechanism and subsequent failure mode	7
Low	Low chance the design control will detect a potential cause / mechanism and subsequent failure mode	6
Moderate	Moderate chance the design control will detect a potential cause / mechanism and subsequent failure mode	5
Moderately High	Moderately high chance the design control will detect a potential cause / mechanism and subsequent failure mode	4
High	High chance the design control will detect a potential cause / mechanism and subsequent failure mode	3
Very High	Very high chance the design control will detect a potential cause / mechanism and subsequent failure mode	2
Almost Certain	Design control will almost certainly detect a potential cause / mechanism and subsequent failure mode	1

The Data Door Routemap – Finding The Right Tool

Graphical tools are the starting point for the Data Door. Theories and ideas that are gained from the graphical analysis can then be investigated with more advanced statistical techniques.

For analysing the data graphically...

Looking at distributions...
- Histogram (p104), Dot Plots (p105)
- Minitab's Graphical Summary (p106)
- Probability Plot (p107)

Looking for changes over time...
- Time Series Plot (p109)

Comparing distributions or groups of data...
- Box Plot (p116) and Individual Value Plot (p119)

Comparing proportions and percentages...
- 100% Stacked Bar Chart (p121)

Looking for relationships between two sets of data...
- Scatter Plot (p122), Matrix Plot (p123)

Looking at different categories of data...
- Pareto Chart (p112)

For analysing the data statistically...

Deciding if a distribution fits a particular model (e.g. Normal)
- Normality Test (Anderson Darling) (p159)
- Individual Distribution Identification (p161)

Deciding if changes over time are significant
- Statistical Process Control (SPC) (p195)
- Run Charts (p110)

Deciding if groups of data are different, and quantifying the difference...
- Confidence Intervals (p125) & Hypothesis testing (p128)

Quantifying the relationships between process inputs and outputs...
- Correlation & Regression (p163)
Simple Regression (p167), Fitted Line Plots (p168),
Multiple Regression (p171), Binary Logistic Regression (p173)

Adjusting the process to look for relationships between its inputs and outputs...
- Design of Experiments (DOE) (p177)

Minitab's 'Display Descriptive Statistics'

The first Minitab command used on most data is 'Display Descriptive Statistics'. It provides a range of statistics for your data and offers a basic range of graphs.

Minitab: Stat > Basic Statistics > Display Descriptive Stats

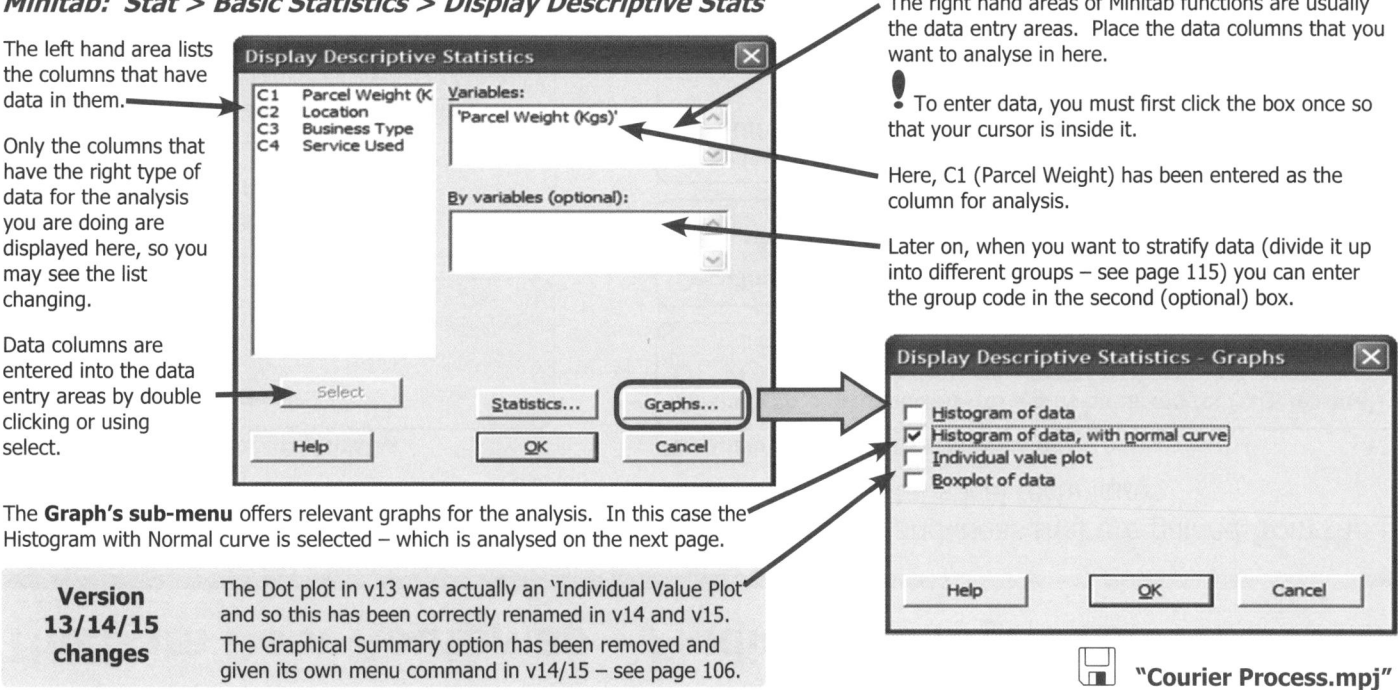

The left hand area lists the columns that have data in them.

Only the columns that have the right type of data for the analysis you are doing are displayed here, so you may see the list changing.

Data columns are entered into the data entry areas by double clicking or using select.

The right hand areas of Minitab functions are usually the data entry areas. Place the data columns that you want to analyse in here.

To enter data, you must first click the box once so that your cursor is inside it.

Here, C1 (Parcel Weight) has been entered as the column for analysis.

Later on, when you want to stratify data (divide it up into different groups – see page 115) you can enter the group code in the second (optional) box.

The **Graph's sub-menu** offers relevant graphs for the analysis. In this case the Histogram with Normal curve is selected – which is analysed on the next page.

Version 13/14/15 changes	The Dot plot in v13 was actually an 'Individual Value Plot' and so this has been correctly renamed in v14 and v15. The Graphical Summary option has been removed and given its own menu command in v14/15 – see page 106.

"Courier Process.mpj"

Histograms (sometimes called Frequency Plots)

Histograms are one of the most common Six Sigma tools. They show the shape of the distribution and form an essential part of the '1st Pass Analysis' of any data (see page 71) .

This histogram is the output from the previous page. It represents the distribution of parcel weights found in a courier company.

Minitab scales the axis automatically, but if you want a certain range to be displayed, you can set them yourself by double clicking the axis (v14/15).

"Courier Process.mpj"

Histogram (with Normal Curve) of Parcel Weight (Kgs)

Mean	3.612
StDev	0.6441
N	100

Frequency axis: 0, 2, 4, 6, 8, 10, 12, 14, 16

Parcel Weight (Kgs) axis: 2.4, 3.0, 3.6, 4.2, 4.8, 5.4

Sample size: Histograms often get used without any indication of the amount of data that they are based on. This is not only bad practice, but leads to observations being made on very little data.

Minitab versions 14 & 15 provide a summary of the mean, variation and sample size on the histogram.

The minimum sample size for a histogram is 25. Watch out for histograms that have very few columns like the one shown below, since this can indicate that the sample was small, or that the measurement system had low resolution (p56).

Interpreting Histograms: The golden rule when analysing histograms is not to read too much into them. Instead, the results should be summarised using day to day language. For example;

> *"this histogram shows that the parcel weights range from about 2kgs up to 5.5kgs, with most of the parcels being between 3 and 4.5"*

or *"the distribution looks symmetric around the average parcel weight of 3.6kgs, and appears to fit the Normal distribution curve".*

An example of a histogram with too few columns (indicating a small sample size)....

Dot Plots

Dot plots are an alternative to histograms and are also a form of 'Frequency Distribution'. Histograms are widely used and suitable for most applications, but Dot Plots offer some other features.

This Dot Plot shows the same parcel weight data contained in the histogram on the previous page. Usually every dot represents a piece of data, (but when there's lots of data, each point may represent 4 or 5 results).

The Dot Plot will use a different number of columns from the histogram and so the **exact** shapes are not the same. However, the **overall** shape is the same as the histogram (it is the same data).

Minitab: Graph > Dot plot

'Brushed' area:

Sample Size: 100

2.0　2.5　3.0　3.5　4.0　4.5　5.0

The brushing function in Minitab allows you to investigate graphs such as the Dot Plot to see which data points are which. With brushing 'on', a rectangle has been dragged over the last few points on this Dot Plot. At the same time, a small window appears with the row numbers of the 'brushed' data, and the relevant rows are also highlighted in the worksheet.

Minitab: Editor > Brush

💾　**"Courier Process.mpj"**

Brushing ✕

Row
4
15
22
24
45
65

Dot Plot or Histogram?　They are both frequency distributions and so the overall shape of the distribution will be the same. Which graph to use depends on your application/preference:

▪ Histograms summarise the data well and can be useful for presentations.

▪ Dot Plots usually show one dot for every data point which allows Minitab's graph 'Brushing' function (p14) to be used.

Minitab's 'Graphical Summary'

Minitab's Graphical Summary provides a range of useful outputs for analysing a column of data.

Minitab: **Stat > Basic Statistics > Graphical Summary - v14 and 15**
Stat > Basic Statistics > Display Descriptive Stats > Graphs menu - v13

This Graphical Summary shows an analysis of the time it takes from receiving an order to shipping it, at an online retailer's warehouse.

The **histogram** shows a process ranging from about 1.5 hours to 6 hours and the process **does not** appear to fit the Normal curve very well; appearing slightly skewed to the left.

The **Box plot** (see page 116) summarises the distribution of the data, and uses the same scale as the histogram.

The **Confidence Intervals** for the Mean and Median are displayed, but it is important to note that this diagram has its own scale, and so cannot be compared directly with the histogram above.

The Anderson Darling Normality Test is explained on page 159. In this example, a p-value of 0.005 (very low) indicates the process is definitely **not** Normally distributed.

Mean, Standard deviation and Sample Size are summarised here.
(Skewness and Kurtosis are not dealt with in this text.)

The information on quartiles is used to generate the Box plot (page 116).

The limits of the Confidence Intervals for the mean, median and standard deviation are summarised here.

Summary for Time to ship (Decimal hours)

Sample Size: 100

Anderson-Darling Normality Test
A-Squared 2.59
P-Value < 0.005

Mean 2.9640
StDev 1.0232
Variance 1.0470
Skewness 0.509477
Kurtosis -0.764200
N 100

Minimum 1.6000
1st Quartile 2.1000
Median 2.8000
3rd Quartile 3.9000
Maximum 5.8000

95% Confidence Interval for Mean
2.7610 3.1670
95% Confidence Interval for Median
2.4000 3.0000
95% Confidence Interval for StDev
0.8984 1.1886

95% Confidence Intervals

Confidence Intervals (CI) are explained in detail on page 125, but for now, a practical definition of a confidence interval for the mean (average) is:

*"you can be 95% confident that the mean **time to ship** for this process lies within the limits of the confidence interval shown here".*

Probability Plots

So far in this text, histograms with Normal curves have been the main method for deciding if a data set fits the Normal distribution. Probability plots can provide a more decisive approach.

What are probability plots?

Trying to decide if a histogram is 'Normally' distributed can be a very subjective decision.

Probability plots are intended to help answer the question by plotting the data in a different format. A probability plot is constructed in a way that the points will fall in a straight line if they fit the distribution in question (e.g. Normal). This is a useful technique, since the human eye is better at assessing if something is straight or not.

The **vertical axis** represents estimated cumulative probability. The key point to note is that the scale is not linear (it is more like a logarithmic scale), and it is symmetrical around 50% (much like the Normal curve). So, this scaling of the axis is what creates a straight line if the data **is** Normally distributed.

Minitab: Graph > Probability Plot (Gives 95% CI Limits)
or   Stat > Basic Statistics > Normality Test (No 95% CI Limits)

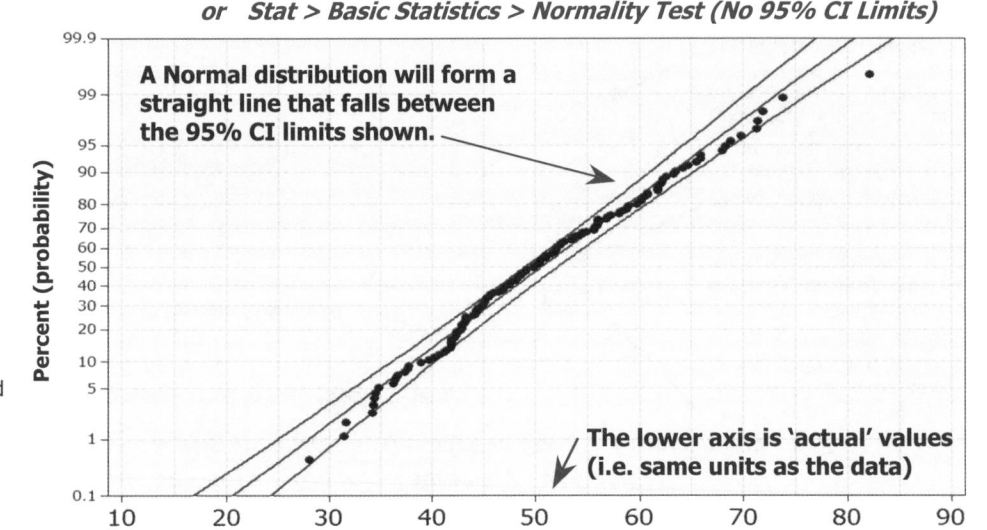

A Normal distribution will form a straight line that falls between the 95% CI limits shown.

The lower axis is 'actual' values (i.e. same units as the data)

So, how straight should the line be?

Just as histograms are never perfectly smooth, the line will never be perfectly straight, even if the data is Normal. So Minitab places 95% CI limits on the diagram and if all the points fall within the lines, you can assume the data is Normally distributed.

Probability plots in practice: Even probability plots do not provide a clear cut answer all the time, but they are an improvement. Points at the extremes are more likely to be outside of the 95% CI limits, so do not decide your data does not fit the distribution just because of one or two points.

The page below contains two further examples to help you decide.

Probability Plots (cont.)

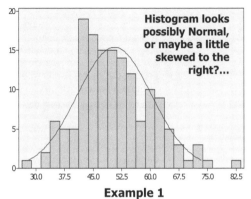

Histogram looks possibly Normal, or maybe a little skewed to the right?...

Example 1

...but the probability indicates it *can* be assumed to be Normal.

The examples shown here are from this data file: **"Distributions.mpj"**

Example 1 on the left (column C2 in the data file) is **actually** from a Normal distribution, but on a histogram it **appears** to be slightly skewed to the right.

However, the probability plot shows a straight line that falls mainly between the limits, and so it can be correctly concluded that the data **is** Normally distributed.

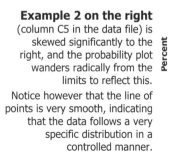

Example 2 on the right (column C5 in the data file) is skewed significantly to the right, and the probability plot wanders radically from the limits to reflect this.

Notice however that the line of points is very smooth, indicating that the data follows a very specific distribution in a controlled manner.

Histogram shows that the process is significantly skewed to the right...

Example 2

...and the probability plot confirms this.

Percent

Time Series Plots

Time Series plots combined with Histograms are the two most important graphical tools in Six Sigma.

Time Series plots can help you to spot changes and trends over time that histograms just cannot see.

Things to look out for are...

- Upwards or downwards trends
- Changes in the amount of variation
- Difference between the short and the long term
- Patterns or cycles in the data.
- Anything that doesn't appear to be random

Time Series Plots in practice:

Be careful not to read too much into the charts. It is easy to see trends that are not actually there, or to draw conclusions on only a few data points. If there is something worth finding it will usually be obvious.

If you decide you need a more advanced technique for assessing the stability of a process over time, you could try a Run Chart (next page) or SPC chart (page 195), both of which are essentially more advanced Time Series plots.

Minitab: Graph > Time Series Plot

This plot shows the weight of parcels (over time) taken from the courier process plotted in the histogram on page 104. It looks reasonably random and stable.

Time ordered data:

Time Series Plots require data that is in the order that it actually happened. This may sound obvious but it is often forgotten (or ignored), making a Time Series plot meaningless.

Other examples...

This process appears to have two different levels. Perhaps it's two separate processes?

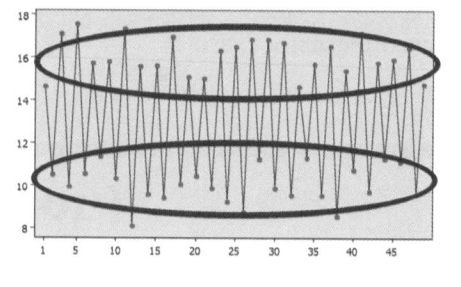

This process appears to have a repeated pattern, with an upward trend?

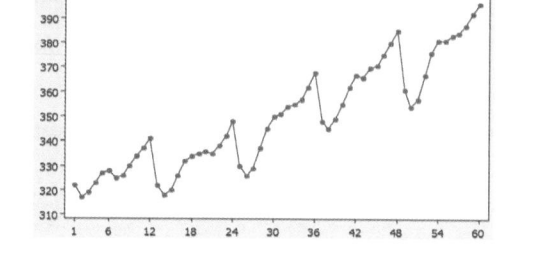

Run Charts

Run charts provide a more sophisticated method of deciding if your process is stable.

Sometimes it can be difficult to decide if your process is stable, just by looking at a Time Series plot. Conversely, it can be easy to read too much into time series plots and start seeing trends that are not actually there!

Run charts are a quick and easy approach to deciding if your process is statistically stable.

Example: A kitchen equipment manufacturer is finding that some of their saucepan lids don't fit the saucepans. One theory is that the diameter of the saucepans is varying because the production process is unstable. To investigate the problem, the diameter of the saucepans is monitored and recorded in Minitab.

25 saucepans are measured (you need at least 20 or more data points for a Run Chart) and Minitab's Run Chart function is used to analyse the results.

If your data is in a single column, then check the **single column** box and enter the column containing the data here.

If your data was collected in subgroups (a few measurements taken at the same time) then enter the column that contains the subgroup number in **Subgroup size**. If in doubt, or if your data was not collected in subgroups, enter a subgroup size of 1.

Minitab: Stat > Quality Tools > Run Chart

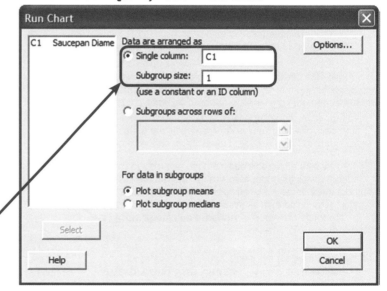

"Run Chart-Diameters.mpj"

Run Charts (cont.)

Run Charts work by analysing the **actual** number of runs in your data points and comparing them to the **expected** number of runs (for the amount of data that you have). If there's a big difference between the actual and the expected, then it is likely that your process has some special cause variation, and you should investigate further.

Interpreting Run Charts: Minitab analyses two different types of run – runs about the median, and runs up or down.

1) Runs about the median: A single run about the median is a number of consecutive data points that all fall the same side of the median line. A run stops when the line crosses the median. In this case there are seven groups (runs) of data that fall the same side of the median.

▪ If the p-value for clustering is below 0.05 (as in this case) then there are statistically fewer runs than expected, and this suggests that there is some 'clustering' within the data.
▪ If the p-value for mixtures is below 0.05 then there are statistically too many runs in the data, and this suggests that there is some mixing of different processes in the data.

2) Runs up or down: A single run up or down, is a number of consecutive data points that all increase or decrease. A run stops when the direction of the line (up or down) changes. In this case there are nineteen groups (runs) of data that either go up or down.

▪ If the p-value for trends is below 0.05 then there are statistically fewer runs than expected, and this suggests that there are some trends within the data.
▪ If the p-value for oscillation is below 0.05 then there are statistically too many runs in the data. This suggests that the process is not stable, but instead is varying up and down too rapidly.

Interpreting this example: In this example, the only p-value that is below 0.05, is the p-value for clustering (0.004). This suggests that there is unexpectedly high clustering within the data. This observation requires investigation, but the key conclusion is that the process is not completely random and **does** have some level of special cause variation. The clustering suggests the process output is drifting over time, and this might explain why the saucepan lids don't always fit!

Pareto Analysis – Data Input

Paretos are used to help identify the most common categories in a column of textual data. They are most commonly used for 'reason code' data, but Paretos can be used on any categorical data.

Example: A project looking at postage delays took a sample of 240 delayed postage items and recorded the reason for the delay in each case. In addition, it was recorded if the postage had originated in a rural or urban location. There are two options for storing this data in Minitab as explained below.

Minitab: Stat > Quality Tools > Pareto Chart

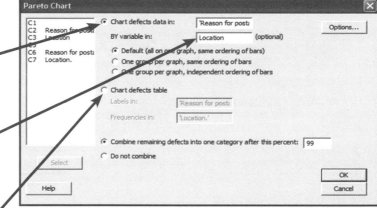

⊟ **"Pareto-Postage.mpj"**

Option 1: 'Chart defects data in' should be used when the data is in its raw form (contained in one column as below).

For this example if two Pareto charts are required (one for each of the urban/rural locations) then the optional '**by variable in**' should be completed. Otherwise leave blank.

C2-T	C3-T
Reason for postage delay	**Location**
Not franked	urban
No Postcode	urban
No Stamp	rural
No Stamp	urban
Postcode unreadable	rural
No Postcode	urban
Not franked	urban

Option 2: **"Chart defects table"** should be used when the data has been recorded as a table, as shown here (right).
Using this option, the data cannot be divided out by urban/rural locations.

The Pareto analysis of *all* the data is shown on the next page.
The Pareto analysis of the data separated by urban/rural locations is shown on the subsequent page.

C6-T	C7
Reason for postage delay.	**Location.**
Not franked	42
No Stamp	76
No Postcode	98
Postcode unreadable	14
No address	6
Wrong postage	4

Pareto Analysis – Minitab Output

What are Pareto charts?

Pareto charts are essentially frequency plots for categorical / contextual data (see page 52), where the most frequent results are placed in order from the left hand side of the charts.

The **Cumulative Frequency** is also plotted (as a line) and shows the total (cumulative) count of all the reason codes combined from the left of the chart. The table at the bottom gives the exact numerical results.

Interpreting this example:

For this example, 'No Postcode' is the most frequent reason for delay with 98 found (40.8%), and 'No Stamp' is the second most frequent, with 76 found (31.7%). **Together** (cumulatively) they represent 72.5% of the failures found – shown by the cumulative curve.

The 80/20 Principle:

Reasons for failure are often found to conform to the **80/20 principle** which says that 80% of the failures are generally caused by around 20% of the problems.

This effect can be seen to some extent in this example, since the first two reasons for postal delay (out of 6) create 72.5% of the failures.

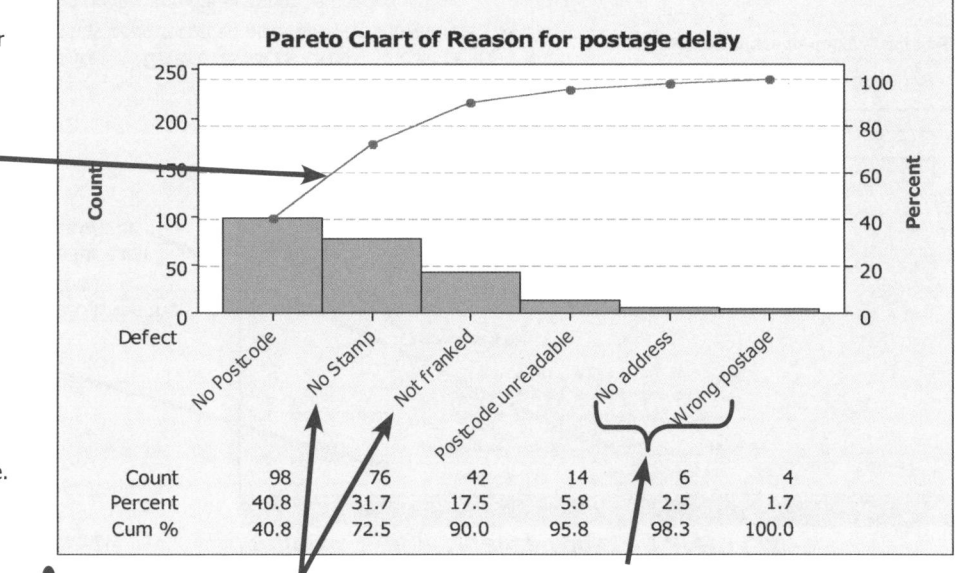

Pareto Chart of Reason for postage delay

	No Postcode	No Stamp	Not franked	Postcode unreadable	No address	Wrong postage
Count	98	76	42	14	6	4
Percent	40.8	31.7	17.5	5.8	2.5	1.7
Cum %	40.8	72.5	90.0	95.8	98.3	100.0

Watch out for similar reason codes. In this example, the reasons 'No Stamp' and 'Not Franked' could have been combined into a 'No Payment' category, which would have been more frequent than 'No Postcode' and changed the Pareto chart completely. However, only reason codes that have the same root cause should be combined.

The 'Other' category: You may find that you have lots of very small categories that are not of interest. The Pareto chart can be set to combine all categories after a certain point into one. This Pareto chart was constructed with this option set at 99% (see previous page). Using the default of 95% would have combined the last two categories into one, called 'other'.

Pareto Analysis – Minitab Output (cont.)

As explained on page 112, the 'by variable in' box can be used when constructing a Pareto chart in order to produce separate charts for different categories. This can be useful if you want to compare the frequency of different failure types across several different locations, machines or departments etc.

In the example output shown here, the data has been separated out by the two different locations – rural and urban.

Why aren't the biggest bars on the left anymore?

Because the 'Default' display option was selected, which places the charts on the same page - with the same ordering of the bars. The 'No Postcode' category has been placed furthest to the left on both charts because it is the largest category overall.

> ❗ **Watch out for reduced sample sizes:** Be careful when separating your data out into subgroups. If you had six different locations, (not just urban/rural) then you would have ended up with 6 different Pareto charts. This may sound more detailed, but at the same time the amount of data in each Pareto chart will reduce very quickly, and you have to make sure that your Pareto charts still contain enough data to be meaningful.

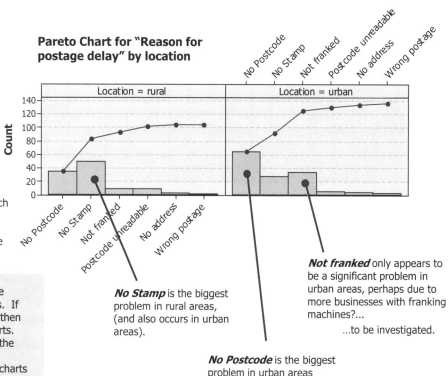

Pareto Chart for "Reason for postage delay" by location

No Stamp is the biggest problem in rural areas, (and also occurs in urban areas).

No Postcode is the biggest problem in urban areas (and also occurs in rural areas).

Not franked only appears to be a significant problem in urban areas, perhaps due to more businesses with franking machines?...

...to be investigated.

Data Stratification

Analysing the differences between subgroups of data can provide clues and insights into how the process behaves. The process of dividing the data into subgroups is called stratification.

Databases often contain lots of categorical information about the environment from which the data was taken. Without it there is no way of investigating many of the theories and ideas that you will have developed.

Example - The data below is a sample of parcel weights from a courier process. Categorical information on the location, business and service was collected along with the weight of the parcels, and this can now be used to further understand the process.

Categorical data that provides information on the different subgroups within the data.

Parcel Weight	Location	Business Type	Service Used
3.4	England	Commercial	Normal
3.99	England	Commercial	Express
4.31	England	Commercial	Normal
5.33	France	Commercial	Overnight
3.84	England	Commercial	Normal
2.82	France	Residential	Express

 "Courier-Process.mpj"

Why divide up the data?

- The differences between your subgroups may be a substantial cause of the variation in your process.
- Identifying subgroups that are different can lead onto an analysis of *why* they are different:

> - the 'best' performing subgroups can be investigated for benchmarking opportunities.

> - the root causes of the 'worst' performing subgroups can be investigated using 5 Why's, fishbone diagrams etc.

Questions that might be answered by stratifying the data...

- Is there a difference in parcel weights between countries?
- Do commercial customers send heavier parcels?
- Do residential customers send a bigger variety of parcel weights?
- Does the weight of the parcel influence the service used?

Graphical tools for analysing and comparing subgroups:

- **Box plots** (page 116) – useful for comparing subgroups that have at least 25 data points in them.
- **Individual Value plots** (page 119) – similar to Box plots, but used with smaller subgroups (less than 25).
- **100% Stacked Bar Chart** (page 121) – useful for comparing proportions within Attribute data.

Box Plots – Introduction

Whenever you are comparing distributions against each other – think Box plots!!

How Box plots work:

Box plots take key statistics from the data and summarise them in a box and whiskers format.

The box represents 50% of the data, starting at Quartile 1 (Q1) and finishing at Q3.

The whiskers represent the range of the data (minimum to maximum).

Outliers: The whiskers can only go out so far (they can only be as long as 1.5 times the length of the box).

Any data results beyond that point are considered to be 'outliers' and are represented with an asterisk: ✳

The middle line of the box is the median, **not** the average.

Some of the box plots in Minitab can also place a dot on the box plot to represent the average.

Different formats: Box plots can be drawn horizontally or vertically.

Sometimes the *width* of the box represents the sample size, but usually it has no significance.

❗ Don't use Box plots if you're looking at just one distribution – histograms are much better. Box plots should be used when comparing several distributions.

Minitab: Box plots can be found under:
- Graph > Box plot
- Display Descriptive Statistics (p103)
- Graphical Summary (p106)
- 2 Sample T-test (p134)

See page 120 for more information

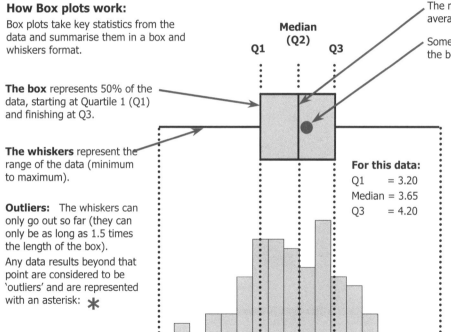

Median (Q2) Q1 Q3

For this data:
Q1 = 3.20
Median = 3.65
Q3 = 4.20

Box Plots – Data Input and Analysis

Minitab: Graph > Box plot

For versions 14 & 15, you must select a Box plot '**with groups**' in order to compare several subgroups of data against each other on the same plot.

The Express service *appears* to be used for parcels of a lower median weight than the Normal service.

n = 42

n = 48

n = 10

Parcel Weight (Kgs)

Express   Normal   Overnight

Boxplot - One Y, With Groups

C1   Parcel Weight (Kgs)
C2   Location
C3   Business Type
C4   Service Used

Graph variables:
'Parcel Weight (Kgs)'   **Enter the data to be plotted here**

Categorical variables for grouping (1-4, outermost first):
'Service Used'   **Enter the column containing the sub-groups here.**

The variation (range) of parcel weights *appears* to be the roughly the same for the Express and Normal services.

"Courier-Process.mpj"

Sample Sizes: Box plots should not be used for subgroups that have less than 25 data points because the size of the box and whiskers can vary significantly. In this example, the 'Overnight' subgroup (shown above) has a sample size of just 10, which makes the calculation of quartiles very variable.

Box Plots – Data Input and Analysis (cont.)

Minitab: Graph > Box plot

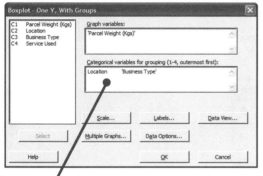

Entering two columns into the categorical variable box will stratify the data by both variables.

The order in which they are entered is important. In this case, the location was entered first, and so the Box plot (right) shows the data stratified by location first, then by the business type.

Once again, be careful of sample sizes (shown on the right). This technique can create a lot of subgroups, but each one may contain very little data. It might be worthwhile trying an Individual Value Plot instead (next page) if your sample sizes are less than 25.

Observations of interest from this Box plot:

- Parcels from Residential customers *appear* to have lower (median) weights than those from Commercial customers.

- This difference *appears* in both France and England. In fact the results for France and England are very similar overall.

- All the subgroups *appear* to have similar levels of variation in parcel weight (the height of the Box plots is similar).

 "Courier-Process.mpj"

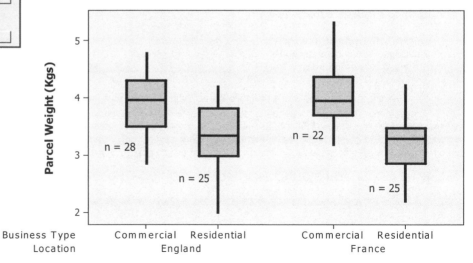

Individual Value Plots

Individual Value Plots should be used in preference to Box plots when the sample size is low (<25).

This Individual Value Plot represents the same data as the Box Plot for parcel weights shown earlier on page 117.

Individual Value Plots provide more 'feel' on the distribution of the data, and can be useful for spotting outliers.

'Jitter': Minitab can spread the data points out from left to right so that they do not overlap. This is called 'Jitter' and can be adjusted in version 15 by double clicking on the data points and selecting Jitter under the Identical Points tab. With Jitter, every Individual Value plot will look slightly different, since Jitter is a random effect. Turning off Jitter will place all the data points on a straight vertical line.

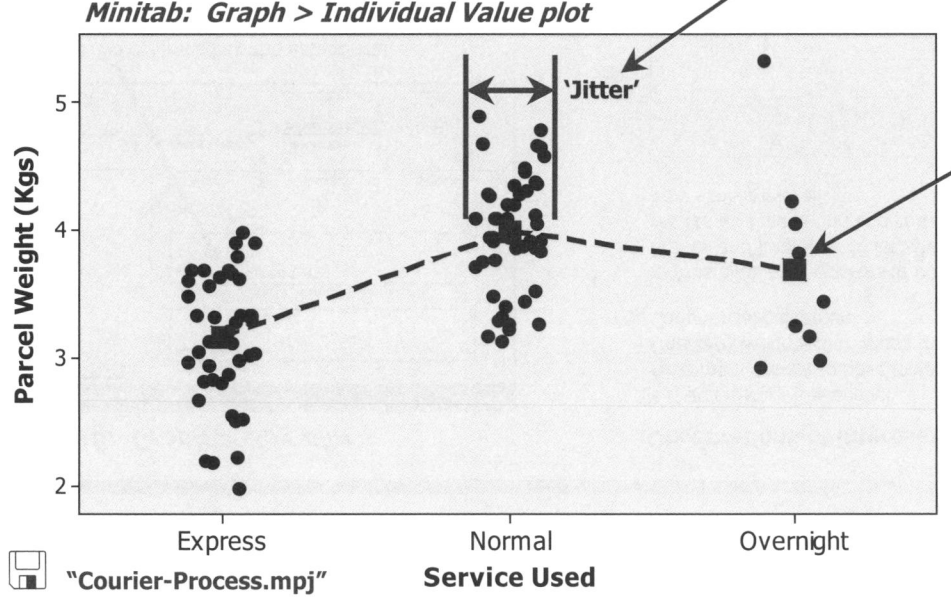

Minitab: Graph > Individual Value plot

'Jitter'

Parcel Weight (Kgs)

Express   Normal   Overnight

Service Used

💾 **"Courier-Process.mpj"**

The smaller **sample size** of the "Overnight" subgroup is immediately obvious with an Individual Value Plot.

This plot was actually created using Minitab's ANOVA function, which shows the subgroup averages (as squares) connected by a dashed line.

Minitab's Brush function (p14) can be used on Individual Value Plots since each point represents an individual piece of data.

Minitab: Like most graphs, Individual Value Plots (IVPs) can be found in several different menu locations in Minitab. However, versions 13, 14 and 15 have some specific differences with respect to IVPs, which are explained on the next page.

Finding Box Plots and Individual Value Plots in Minitab

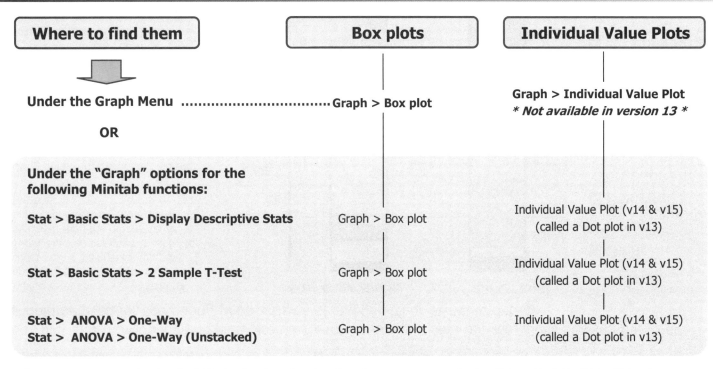

Where to find them	Box plots	Individual Value Plots

Under the Graph Menu .... Graph > Box plot

OR

Graph > Individual Value Plot
* Not available in version 13 *

Under the "Graph" options for the following Minitab functions:

Stat > Basic Stats > Display Descriptive Stats   Graph > Box plot   Individual Value Plot (v14 & v15) (called a Dot plot in v13)

Stat > Basic Stats > 2 Sample T-Test   Graph > Box plot   Individual Value Plot (v14 & v15) (called a Dot plot in v13)

Stat > ANOVA > One-Way
Stat > ANOVA > One-Way (Unstacked)   Graph > Box plot   Individual Value Plot (v14 & v15) (called a Dot plot in v13)

Subgroup Averages: The Hypothesis Testing functions also show the subgroup averages on the Box Plots and Individual Value Plots. Even though you may not want to use the statistical output of the 2 Sample T-test or ANOVA, it is often worth using them in order to see the averages of your subgroups on the plots.

100% Stacked Bar Charts

Box plot and Individual Value plots are useful for Continuous data but the 100% Stacked Bar Chart should be used for comparing **proportions** of categorical or Attribute data.

Whilst Pareto charts are useful for analysing the proportions of reason codes within a single sample, the 100% Stacked bar chart is useful for demonstrating the difference in proportions between 2 or more samples.

Using data from the project looking at reasons for postage delays (see page 112), the frequency in each category is recorded and used with Excel's 100% Stacked Bar Chart function.

Like Pareto charts, the **sample size** is not automatically shown on this chart. It's good practice to make a note of the relevant samples sizes when analysing or presenting this type of graph.

"Pareto-Postage.mpj"

Excel Graph Function: "100% Stacked Bar"

Legend:
- ■ Other
- □ Postcode unreadable
- ■ Not franked
- □ No Stamp
- ■ No Postcode

Rural — **Sample size (n) = 104**

Urban — **Sample size (n) = 136**

Scatter Plots

Any time you are investigating whether a 'relationship' exists between two factors, a scatter plot is the best first step for analysing the data graphically.

The example here is from a project looking at the time taken to answer calls at a call centre.

Over 80 shifts, the average call answer time (for the shift) was recorded alongside the number of people working on that shift.

The diagram shows that a relationship *appears* to exist where the higher the number of personnel available, the lower the average time to answer.

Cause and Effect: Be careful before concluding that a direct 'cause and effect' relationship exists. In this case it seems rational that more personnel will make more people available to answer calls quickly. However, the sales of ice cream would probably correlate against the incidents of sunburn, but there is clearly no direct cause and effect.

Data Types: Scatter plots work with both Continuous and Count data. In this example the Answer Time is Continuous data and the Number of Personnel is Count data.

Minitab: Graph > Scatter Plot (versions 14 & 15)

Graph > Plot (version 13)

"Correlation.mpj"

The Scatter plot is the first step in defining the relationship or correlation between two factors. In cases where the relationship is not so clear, **correlation** (see page 165) can be used to help decide if a relationship exists. **Regression** techniques (see page 167) go a step further and are used to define a relationship (correlation) in a mathematical format.

The simplest of the regression techniques is the Fitted Line Plot, shown on page 168.

The **axis protocol** for scatter plots is that the input to the process should be placed on the X (horizontal) axis and the output from the process on the Y (vertical) axis.

Matrix Plots

Matrix Plots produce an array of Scatter Plots for several columns of data. Potential correlations can then be identified visually for further investigation.

The Scatter Plot on the previous page correlates the average call answer time with the number of people working at a call centre. However the data file also contains data on the incoming volume of calls (average calls per hour) and the time spent on each call (average time per call).

A Matrix Plot is a quick way of producing a Scatter Plot for every combination of these four data columns, allowing a rapid visual assessment of which ones might be related in some way.

So, as we know from the previous page, **answer time** and **number of personnel** are correlated and this stands out clearly here.

The volume of **incoming calls per hour** does not *appear* to be correlated either with **answer time**, with the **number of personnel**, or with the **time per call**, because all of the plots on this row show no obvious trends.

However, there does *appear* to be some relationship between the **time per call** and both **answer time** and **number of personnel**, shown in the first two plots on this row.

Minitab creates mirror images of the plots. So the bottom left plot is the same (but reversed) as the top right plot.

Minitab: Graph > Matrix Plot

"Correlation.mpj"

Explaining the axis units: For this graph, the lower units (1260-1380 personnel) refer to the 'calls per hour', and the 'time per call' units are located at the far left of the matrix (5-7 minutes).

From Graphical Results to Statistical Significance....

Looking back over the last few pages of Box plots and Individual Value plots, you will notice that every time an observation has been made from a graph, the word **'appears'** has been used...
Why?.... Because we cannot actually be sure our observations are true unless we check them statistically.

The graphical results:

The Box plot on the left shows two samples that were taken from two processes A & B. It *appears* that:

- Process A has a lower average than process B, and
- Process A has more variation than process B.

The statistical significance:

- How confident are you that the observations you have made are true?
- Would you stake your life on it!?
- How do you know that these results didn't happen just by chance?
- What if processes A & B actually have the same average and variation, but we just happened to get a few high results when collecting sample B, and more varied results when collecting sample A?

The answer is that, at this point, we have to treat the observations that we have made from the graphical results as theories – to be proven one way or the other using more advanced statistical tests for significance.

What would give you more confidence that your observations are true?

If you collected more data and still got the same results, your confidence that processes A & B are different would probably be increased.

Increased sample size is a major contributor to gaining statistical confidence. The more data you have, the more confident you are.

Hypothesis Testing (page 128) covers a range of statistical tests for significance that can be used to help you reach decisions on your data.

Confidence Intervals (CIs)

Instead of assuming a statistic is absolutely accurate, Confidence Intervals can be used to provide a range within which the true process statistic is likely to be (with a known level of confidence).

Example: A saw mill is trying to estimate the average thickness of its 25mm plywood, to see if it really is 25mm!

Nine sheets of plywood are taken randomly from the process, their thickness measured, and the histogram plotted...

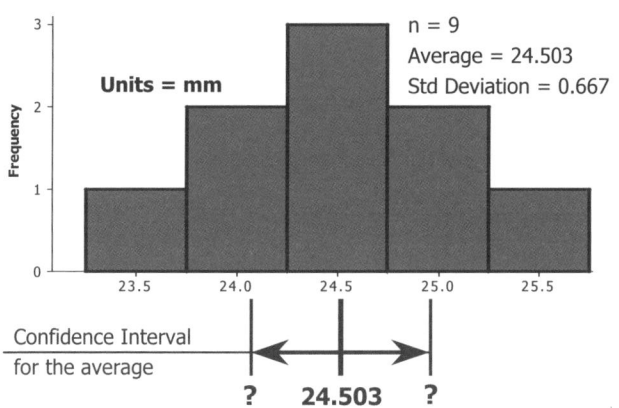

n = 9
Average = 24.503
Std Deviation = 0.667

Confidence Interval for the average

?   **24.503**   ?

The average thickness of the sample turns out to be 24.503mm, not 25mm, and so it *appears* that the plywood sheets are too thin. But does this mean that the whole process is too thin, or that we just happened to select a sample of nine sheets that were on the thin side?

Confidence Intervals can be used to help decide.

(Simplified) mathematical equation for a Confidence Interval:

$$\text{95\% Confidence Interval for the average of the Population} = \text{Sample Average} +/- \text{'t'} \left[\frac{\text{Sample Sigma}}{\sqrt{n} \text{ (square root of n)}} \right]$$

The equation above says that a confidence interval is dependant on:

- **The sample average;** since this is our best estimate at this point.
- **The sample size (n):** As sample size decreases, the confidence interval gets bigger (exponentially) to cope with the fact that less data was collected.
- **The Process variation (Sample Sigma):** The higher the process variation (estimated from the sample) the bigger the confidence interval.
- **The Confidence level required (t):** The value of "t" is taken from statistical tables similar to the Z-table. If a 99% Confidence Interval were required, then the value of "t" would be larger, to increase the interval.

Using the equation above, and a 't' constant of 2.306 (tables not provided), the 95% CI for the average plywood thickness can be calculated as follows:

95% CI = 24.503 +/- 2.306 (0.667 / $\sqrt{9}$) = 24.503 +/- 0.5127
= **23.99mm to 25.02mm**

So, we can be 95% confident that the average thickness of the process is somewhere between 23.99 and 25.02mm. Since this includes 25mm, there is a **chance** that the process is producing an average thickness of 25mm after all.

Confidence Intervals within Minitab's Graphical Summary

Anderson-Darling Normality Test	
A-Squared	0.30
P-Value	0.505
Mean	24.503
StDev	0.667
Variance	0.445
Skewness	0.694460
Kurtosis	-0.115432
N	9
Minimum	23.654
1st Quartile	23.972
Median	24.390
3rd Quartile	25.064
Maximum	25.742

95% Confidence Interval for Mean	
23.990	25.016
95% Confidence Interval for Median	
23.904	25.075
95% Confidence Interval for StDev	
0.450	1.278

95% Confidence Intervals

Median C.I.   Average C.I.

The Confidence Intervals for the Median and Average are also shown graphically here.
(NB: the scale is not shared with the histogram).

"Wood Thickness.mpj"

Minitab's Graphical Summary function (see page 106) provides Confidence Intervals for the Average, Median and Standard Deviation of the process, as shown here for the plywood thickness example introduced on the previous page.

Converting statistics into 'real' language is an important skill for a Six Sigma analyst. The Confidence Intervals shown here can be interpreted into everyday language as follows:

We can be 95% confident that:

- the **average** thickness of the plywood is somewhere between 23.99 and 25.01mm.

    - the **median** thickness of the plywood is somewhere between 23.90 and 25.07.

        - the **standard deviation** of the plywood thickness is somewhere between 0.45 and 1.278

The Confidence *Level* of the intervals (in this case 95%) can be adjusted in Minitab's Graphical Summary function. As the confidence level is increased, the size of the Confidence Intervals increases, because you are demanding **more** confidence that the value is within the interval (this can seem a little counter intuitive). So, for the plywood thickness example:

The 90% CI for the average =	24.1 to 24.9	**90%**
The 95% CI for the average =	24.0 to 25.0	**95%**
The 99% CI for the average =	23.7 to 25.2	**99%**

Confidence Intervals for Proportions

Minitab's **1 Proportion** function can be used to calculate confidence intervals for percentages (Attribute data). You do not need a data file to use the this function since Minitab allows you to enter summarised data directly as follows:

Select the summarised data option, enter the total sample size and the number of events. The definition of an event is up to you. So, if you are looking at a product failure rate, you would enter the number of failures (number of events) in your sample and the total sample size (number of trials).

The 1 Proportion function can also be used to complete a hypothesis test (see page 153). However, in this case we only require a confidence interval, and so this box should be left unchecked (this function is not available on version 13 & 14).

The effect of sample size on the confidence interval.

As explained on page 125, larger sample sizes allow us to be more confident in our results. You can use the 1 Proportion function to demonstrate this relationship. For example, try the following:

Keeping 20% as your percentage, and using different sample sizes…

For a sample size of 50 (10 out of 50), the CI is 10% to 33.7%.
For a sample size of 500 (100 out of 500), the CI is 16.5% to 23.7%.
For a sample size of 1000 (200 out of 1000), the CI is 17.5% to 22.6%.

Minitab: Stat > Basic Statistics > 1 Proportion

Example: A political polling company is interested to find out the percentage of voters that are intending to vote for a liberal party in an upcoming election. A random selection of 100 voters are polled and 20 of them indicate that they would be voting liberal (20%).

However, 100 is not a very large sample (particularly for Attribute data), and so Minitab's 1 Proportion function is used to calculate a confidence interval for the 20% result. The session window results (left) provide a 95% confidence interval of between 12.6% and 29.1%.

This is quite a large interval, and confirms that a poll of just 100 voters does not provide a very precise prediction of the actual result of an election. In reality, political pollsters tend to use a minimum sample size of 1000 people, which provides around +/- 3% precision.

```
Test and CI for One Proportion


Sample   X    N   Sample p         95% CI
1       20   100  0.200000   (0.126656, 0.291843)
```

Hypothesis Testing Overview

If Confidence Intervals mean you can never take a statistic at face value anymore (because there is always some potential for error), how are you going to prove (or disprove) anything?

The short answer is "you're not"!

We can be very certain, even 99.9% certain, but never 100% certain anymore. Hypothesis testing refers to a set of tools that can tell us how certain we can be in making a specific decision or statement. So, we can now place a level of certainty on the observations we make from graphs.

This may sound strange but it is actually a step in the right direction. By telling us how certain (confident) we can be in our decisions, hypothesis testing also tells us our risk of being wrong – something that has rarely been quantified before in business organisations.

In reality, we have always known there was a chance of being wrong but, because we have not had a way of measuring this risk, it has generally been ignored.

However, because Six Sigma is data driven we cannot take this blinkered approach anymore.

Hypothesis testing has its own flow and terminology, shown opposite, and explained on subsequent pages.

If you are having trouble interpreting hypothesis testing results come back to the basics within the flow shown here.

The Flow

What are you testing? (What's your theory?)

How confident do you want to be in your decision?

Select and run the test

Decide if your theory was right or not

The Six Sigma "Speak"

Define the Null Hypothesis Symbol: Ho

Set your Alpha Level

Calculate the p-value (based on your data)

Accept or reject the Null Hypothesis

Convert your decision back into 'normal' terminology

Tossing a Coin – An Everyday Hypothesis Test

This everyday example of tossing a coin demonstrates that the 'hypothesis test' approach is actually something we do quite naturally, without realising it.

A friend of yours says he has a coin that lands on heads more often than it lands on tails. You don't believe him, because we all know that coins are 50/50 in the way they fall, so you ask him to toss the coin a few times, and you'll make up your own mind based on the results **(show me the data!)**

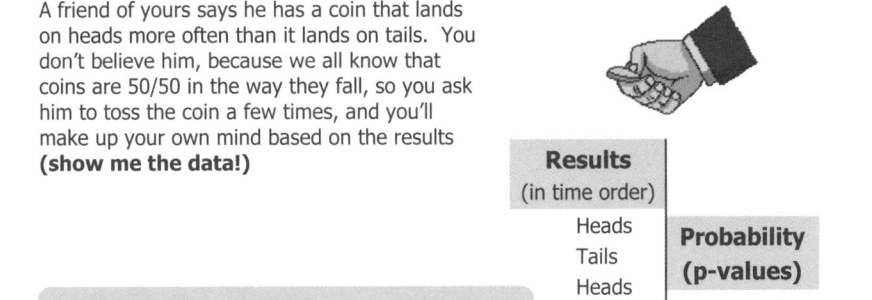

After five throws, it is Heads 80%, Tails 20%. He says that proves it, but you're not so sure.

After ten throws, it is still Heads 80%, Tails 20%. Now you don't know what to think, the data is starting to look like he could be right!

After fifteen throws, it is still Heads 80%, Tails 20%!. Now you're convinced, and you agree with him that coin is not 50/50 because of the results you've seen.

Results (in time order)	Probability (p-values)
Heads	
Tails	
Heads	
Heads	*Not* unlikely
Heads	(37.5%)
Heads	
Heads	
Tails	
Heads	Quite unlikely
Heads	(10.9%)
Heads	
Heads	
Heads	
Tails	Very unlikely
Heads	(3.5%)

What happened?   After every five throws, you reviewed the results, and the percentage of Heads and Tails was the same – always 80/20. So why did it take you so long to decide that the coin was **not** 50/50?

Probably because you were waiting to be more confident in your decision?

From a hypothesis testing point of view; after every five throws, you worked out the probability (the 'p-value') of getting the results you had got, if the coin were 50/50 (your Null Hypothesis).

First hypothesis test: After five throws, 80/20 didn't seem unlikely if the coin was 50/50. The p-value was 0.375.

Second hypothesis test: After ten throws, 80/20 was quite unlikely if the coin was truly 50/50. The p-value was at this point 0.109.

Third hypothesis test: After fifteen throws, 80/20 was very unlikely if the coin was 50/50, so you decided it couldn't be a 50/50 coin, and agreed with your friend. The p-value at this point was 0.035.

When the p-value reached 0.035, we say that it had dropped below your 'alpha level' (p131) – the point at which you decided the Null Hypothesis (50/50 coin) was not very likely, and so you 'rejected the Null hypothesis'.

Confidence Levels and Alpha Levels (a.k.a Alpha Risk)

Before you perform a hypothesis test you must set your 'Alpha Level', which is the level that the p-value must drop below if you are to 'reject the null' and decide there is a difference.

As explained on the previous page, the p-value is related to your confidence in deciding that a difference exists between samples of data. So, you must also decide on how much confidence you want (in saying that a difference exists between samples of data) in order to set the "Alpha Level."

How do you decide on your required confidence? You need to consider the risks of making the wrong decision in order to establish your required confidence. This will often depend on the environment you are working in and the particular decision you are trying to make. Working in a safety critical environment such as an oil platform at sea or in a hospital, you would probably look for higher confidence in your decisions. The key point is that you must decide on your Alpha Level **before** you carry out the Hypothesis test, **not** once you have seen the results!

Example: Your company makes machined components for the aerospace industry and you are currently considering a major investment in new machinery that will (hopefully) resolve some current quality issues. You have two sets of data – one from the current machine, and one from the new machine – and they appear to suggest that the new machine provides an improvement.

Because of the high investment involved you decide you need a confidence level of 95% if you are to purchase the new machinery, and so you will need a p-value of less than 0.05 when comparing the results of the old and new machines.

Example: Your project on call centre customer service is piloting a change to the process flow that appears to improve performance. The proposed change has very little cost and possibly better performance, and so you decide that you only require 90% confidence in your decision. Consequently a p-value less than 0.10 will be enough.

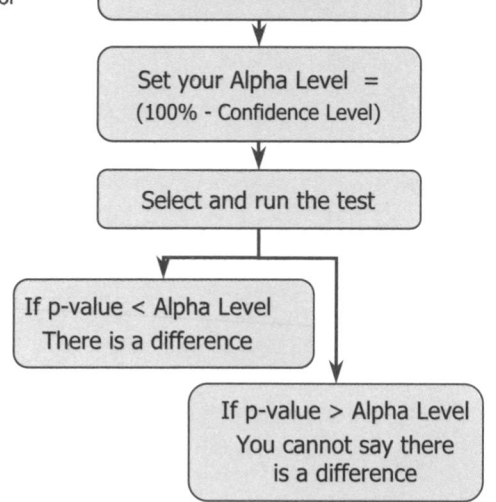

Setting The Right Null Hypothesis (Ho)

The Null and Alternative Hypotheses (Ho & Ha) are always set up in a very similar fashion...
...regardless of whether you think you are going to prove or disprove the Null.

What you are looking at	The Null Hypothesis (Ho)	The Alternative Hypothesis (Ha)
Average call answer times between call centres or operators	There is **no** difference in average call answer time between centres/operators	There **is** a difference in average call answer time between centres/operators
Customer satisfaction levels for different cars	There is **no** difference in customer satisfaction levels between the cars	There **is** a difference in customer satisfaction levels between the cars
The *variation* in a product dimension between different production machines	There is **no** difference in the variation of the dimension from the different machines	There **is** a difference in the variation of the dimension from the different machines
Process waiting times across different regions	There is **no** difference in the waiting times across the different regions	There **is** a difference in waiting times across the different regions

Hypotheses are always the same...

The Null hypothesis always starts with "there is **no** difference" and is therefore very specific.

In reverse, the Alternative always starts with "there **is** a difference" which is not so specific (but that is an important characteristic of hypothesis testing).

Proving or disproving?...

Because of the way they are set up, if you decide that there is a difference between two sets of data (rejecting the Null), a hypothesis test does not tell you how big that difference is, but only that it is there.

This is because you are not **proving** the Alternative Hypothesis, but just finding enough evidence to **disprove** the Null Hypothesis.

Hypothesis Tests for Averages and Medians

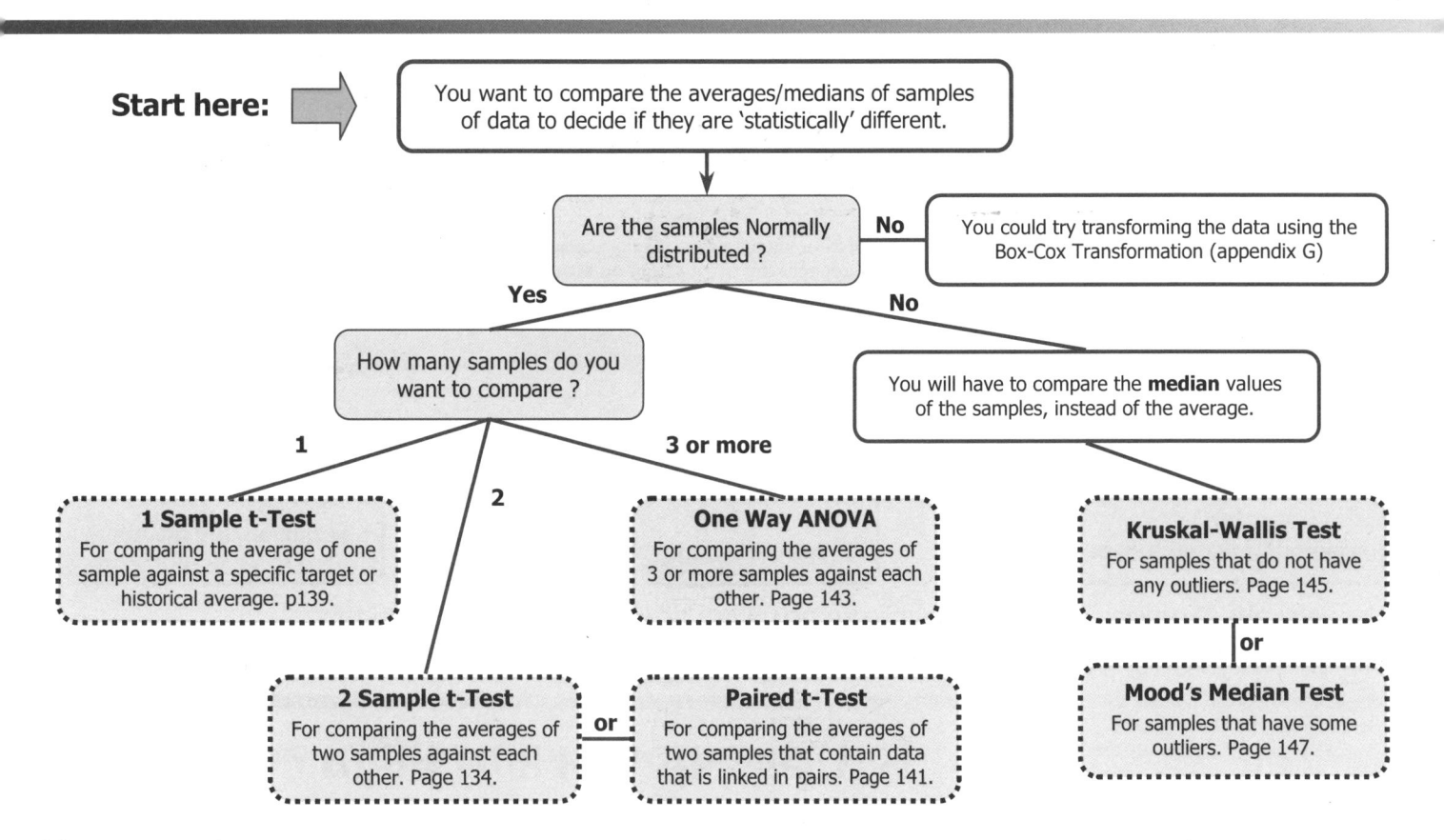

Start here: ⇨ You want to compare the averages/medians of samples of data to decide if they are 'statistically' different.

Are the samples Normally distributed ?

No → You could try transforming the data using the Box-Cox Transformation (appendix G)

Yes

How many samples do you want to compare ?

No → You will have to compare the **median** values of the samples, instead of the average.

1

1 Sample t-Test
For comparing the average of one sample against a specific target or historical average. p139.

2

3 or more

One Way ANOVA
For comparing the averages of 3 or more samples against each other. Page 143.

Kruskal-Wallis Test
For samples that do not have any outliers. Page 145.

or

2 Sample t-Test
For comparing the averages of two samples against each other. Page 134.

or

Paired t-Test
For comparing the averages of two samples that contain data that is linked in pairs. Page 141.

Mood's Median Test
For samples that have some outliers. Page 147.

2 Sample t-test – Some Preliminary Issues

A 2 sample t-test looks at differences in the averages of two different samples. Many of the issues described here also apply to the other Hypothesis tests on subsequent pages.

What does 2 different "samples" mean?

This could mean you have samples of data from two different machines, time periods, geographies, departments, processes or methods etc.

❗ Be careful not to get confused with terminology. The **number** of samples (in this case 2) is different from the samples' **sizes**. For example:
- the *first sample* may have a *sample size* of 30 'pieces' of data.
- the *second sample* may have a *sample size* of 150.

Does the data need to be Normally distributed for a t-test?

In theory, the data *should* be Normally distributed for a 2 sample t-test. This means that *each separate* sample of data that you have should be Normally distributed.

In reality, if your sample distributions are smooth and 'roughly' Normal, then go ahead and try a t-test. Of course, if you are using a 2 sample t-test on data that is not Normal, and you plan to spend large sums of money based on the results, then it might be a little dangerous! (and you should worry about your approach to reaching decisions – Six Sigma or not!).

In the end it is all about taking a logical and practical approach.

Alternatively, you could test for a difference in the medians of the samples using the Kruskal-Wallis or Mood's Median tests, since these tests do not require Normally distributed samples (see previous page).

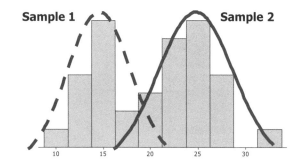

Do the two samples have to be the same size?

No. The test takes account of the different sample sizes involved and adjusts the result accordingly.

What if my data is not reliable, and I don't think I'll see a difference even if there is one?

You shouldn't be here! If your data is not reliable, you shouldn't be trying to analyse it. Instead, go back to the Measure phase and look at Measurement System Analysis (page 53). Only if your data represents the process it measures, should you be reaching decisions on it.

2 Sample t-test — Putting the Data into Minitab

As with many tests, the 2 sample t-test screen looks more complicated than it really is because it has got different options depending on how your raw data is laid out.

Minitab: Stat > Basic Stat > 2 sample t

If all of your data (from both samples) has been placed together into one column, then use this first option; "samples in one column".

However, you will still need a second column that contains "subscripts", (coded data that indicates which sample each bit of data came from).

Example: The data for this t-test was taken from a project at a shipping company, looking at the number of days it takes for its ships to travel its most lucrative route to Japan.

A new route has been trialed over the last few months to see if it reduces the average number of days for each trip. The data can be found in:

"Two-Sample-T-Shipping.mpj"

The trial route data is labelled 'new'.
The historical route data is labelled 'old'.

If your two samples are in two *different* columns, use this second option.

Using this option, the columns do not need to be the same length, since the amount of data in each sample won't necessarily be the same.

Mintab14 & 15 offer a third **summarised data** option that enables you to enter just the key statistics of each sample (sample size, mean and std. deviation).

This is still enough information for Minitab to complete the t-test, and the statistics can be typed directly into this menu screen.

This '**assume equal variances**' will be discussed in more detail later. It is used when your two samples have similar levels of variation in them, since it can then improve the power of the test slightly. However it is not wrong if you don't click it, so if in doubt, leave it blank.

2 Sample t-test – Graphs and Options

Most of Minitab's hypothesis tests have similar Graphs and Options as follows:

For a two sample t-test, Minitab offers two relevant **Graphs**.

▪ Individual Value Plot (page 119) called a 'dot plot' in version 13.

▪ Box plot (see page 116).

The most important thing about graphs is that you **use** them!
Without them, it is very difficult to interpret your statistical output into a practical decision.   **So, always use at least one graph!**

Minitab: Stat > Basic Stat > 2-Sample t > Graphs

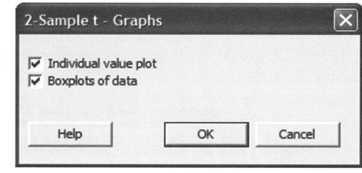

Minitab: Stat > Basic Stat > 2-Sample t > Options

You will find that most of the hypothesis tests have similar **Options** that allow you to make the test more specific, or to change the confidence level etc.

▪ The **Confidence Level** refers to the confidence you require in your decision.

▪ The **Test difference** is effectively your Null hypothesis and should stay at 0.0 if your Null hypothesis is that there is **no** difference (which it is normally is).

▪ The **'Alternative'** refers to the Alternative hypothesis (Ha). Normally the Alternative hypothesis is 'there is a difference' (i.e. not equal). However, Minitab allows you to be more specific and state whether you expect one of the sample means to be less than or greater than the other. This can make your hypothesis test slightly more precise but it is also very easy to get wrong!, so the best advice is not to change this option – always leave as 'not equal'.

2 Sample t-tests — Session Window Results

The trick with hypothesis tests is to make sure you convert them back into real language. No-one wants to hear about your p-values! They just want to know what you have decided, and why.

```
Two-Sample T-Test and CI: Time (days), Route

Two-sample T for Time (days)

Route   N    Mean    StDev   SE Mean
New     20   32.11   3.46    0.77
Old     25   34.35   3.12    0.62


Difference = mu (New) - mu (Old)
Estimate for difference:  -2.237
95% CI for difference:  (-4.250, -0.224)
T-Test of difference = 0 (vs not =): T-Value = -2.25   P-Value = 0.030   DF = 38
```

The first section of the Session Window output is just a summary of the statistics of the samples used in the test.

It can be seen that the sample sizes are different – although this is not a concern for the function of the t-test. The new shipping route has only been done 20 times, to compare with 25 data points for the old route.

These statistics suggest that the average (mean) time for the new route is lower than the old route, by over 2 days (34.35 down to 32.12).

Whether this difference in average is 'real' or not (i.e. statistically significant), is determined by the hypothesis test results below.

Interpreting the 95% CI for the difference:

So, we know from the p-value (opposite) that there is a difference. Minitab actually provides more information on how big the difference is, under *"95% CI for the difference"*.

For this example, we can be 95% confident that the reduction in average shipping time with the new route is somewhere between 0.2 and 4.2 days.

As always, with more data we could be more specific.

Interpreting the p-value: Assuming a confidence level of 95% is required in the decision (an Alpha Level of 0.05)....

The p-value of 0.03 is very low (and more importantly lower than 0.05).

This means that there **is** a difference between the average shipping time of the two routes – so we have **rejected** the Null hypothesis.

To be more specific, our confidence in saying this is actually 97% (=1-0.03).

2 Sample t-tests – Graph Results

The graphical results help to picture what the statistical difference really is.

The Box plots and Individual value plots from the 2 Sample T-test are shown here. The best way to present the findings of a hypothesis test (depending on your audience) is to use graphs like these, combined with a statement that presents the hypothesis test conclusion in day to day language, such as:

" we can be over 95% confident (in fact 97%) that using the new route will reduce our shipping times".

or…

"the data gives us a high degree of confidence that the new route will provide a reduction in average shipping times of between 0.2 and 4.25 days".

Practical versus Statistical Significance:

Both of the charts show that although we have proved a real difference in average, there is still quite a lot of overlap in the results because of the large (natural) variation in the process.

In fact, the reduction of 2 days becomes of less **practical significance** when you consider the range of shipping times is about 10-15 days for both routes.

Although we found an improvement, the data suggests there might be bigger, more important process inputs that we need to find in order to reduce shipping times with more practical significance.

1 Sample t-test — Overview and Example

One sample t-tests allow you to compare the average of just one sample against a known average value, such as an industry benchmark or well established historical average.

Example: Over the last few years (the long term) the time taken to process an invoice has always averaged 16.5 days.

Following a number of minor improvements you measured a small sample of 15 invoices, and found their average time for processing was 15.0

It *appears* that there has been an improvement (reduction) in the average, but the process has lots of variation anyway, and so it is difficult to be sure.

The 1 Sample t-test helps answer the question...

"can you say for sure that your process average is different from the historical average?"

For this example you need to check the **Perform Hypothesis Test** box, and enter 16.5 as your **Hypothesised Mean** (this is the average value that you are comparing your sample against).

The data file for this example can be found in:

 "One-Sample-T.mpj"

Minitab: Stat > Basic Stat > 1-Sample t

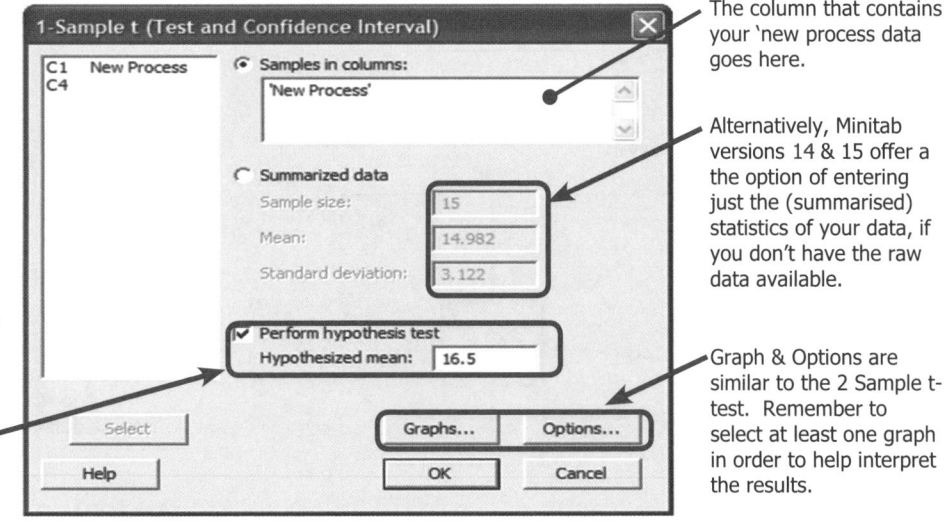

The column that contains your 'new process data goes here.

Alternatively, Minitab versions 14 & 15 offer a the option of entering just the (summarised) statistics of your data, if you don't have the raw data available.

Graph & Options are similar to the 2 Sample t-test. Remember to select at least one graph in order to help interpret the results.

> ❗ Be careful to use 'one sample t' function, **not** the 'one sample Z'. T-tests work with small sample sizes because they compensate for the lower confidence of small samples. The "Z-test" is very similar but doesn't compensate, so you should usually avoid it.

1 Sample t-test — Interpreting the Results

Before you interpret any hypothesis test results, remind yourself what the Null and Alternative hypotheses are for your test. This will help avoid confusion later on when interpreting the p-value.

The Null hypothesis for this example is:

"there is **no** difference between the new process average and the historical average of 16.5"

And the Alternative hypothesis is:

"there **is** a difference between the new process average and the historical average of 16.5"

In addition, you decide that your required confidence is 95% so your Alpha Level is 0.05.

Statistical Results (from Minitab Session window – edited):

Variable	N	Mean	95% CI	T	P
New Process	15	14.9818	(13.2530, 16.7106)	-1.88	0.081

The p-value is 0.081, which is **not** lower than your Alpha Level of 0.05, and so you **cannot** reject the Null..... you **cannot** say there is a difference.

The output also contains the 95% CI for the average of your sample, which runs from 13.25 to 16.7. This interval includes your test mean of 16.5, which is why the test has not been able to prove a difference.

The **graphical results** indicate why the reduction in average is unproven by the hypothesis test result.

The confidence interval for the average of the sample is marked at the bottom of the histogram, and the 'test mean' (16.5) is marked with a large dot. They are clearly overlapping, so they could be the same.

What if we still think there is a difference?

We cannot say that the new process has reduced the average, **but,** be careful how this is interpreted. The hypothesis test is indicating that *with the data available* (just 15 data points), we cannot say the process has improved. It might be that with more data we find a different result but that will take more time to collect.

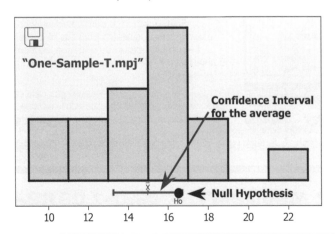

"One-Sample-T.mpj"

Confidence Interval for the average

Null Hypothesis

Paired t-test — Overview and Example

Paired t-tests are similar to 2 sample t-tests, but used where the data samples are linked in **pairs.**

Example: A bank is looking at how long it takes their operators to process customer calls at their call centre.

5 operators have been through a new training program and their processing times for a variety of standard customer requests were recorded before and after the training.

A paired t-test is relevant because it ignores the differences between the operators, and just tests the difference between the pairs of results – before and after training – for each operator.

The Paired t-test helps answer the question...

> **"can you say for sure that there is a difference in processing time between the 'before' and 'after' training results? (ignoring the difference between operators)"**

 "Paired T-Test-Training.mpj"

Minitab: Stat > Basic Stat > Paired t

Paired t (Test and Confidence Interval)

C1	Operator
C2	Before
C3	After
C4	Difference

◉ Samples in columns
First sample: | Before |
Second sample: | After |

○ Summarized data (differences)
Sample size:
Mean:
Standard deviation:

Paired t evaluates the first sample minus the second sample.

Select

Graphs...   Options...

Help   OK   Cancel

❗ The graphs available for the Paired t-test show the **differences** between the pairs of data, not the absolute values (see next page).

❗Minitab assumes the pairs of data are on the same row, as shown below:

Operator	Before	After
1	70.7	64.7
2	60.8	56.9
3	54.1	49.1
1	62.8	57.5
4	61.8	59.1
2	60.7	55.8
3	43.8	39.1
5	52.9	46.6
4	63.6	58.7
1	59.0	55.7

Paired t-test − Interpreting the Results

```
Paired T for Before - After

              N    Mean    StDev   SE Mean
Before       40   60.92    9.46    1.50
After        40   55.98    9.47    1.50
Difference   40    4.943   0.987   0.156

95% CI for mean difference: (4.627,  5.258)
T-Test of mean difference = 0 (vs not = 0): T-Value = 31.68  P-Value = 0.000
```

The average difference in processing time before and after training is a reduction of 4.9 seconds.

More precisely the 95% confidence interval for this difference says that the reduction is at least 4.6 seconds and may be as high as 5.2 seconds.

Statistical results:

The p-value is very low (0.000) which means that the Null Hypothesis can be rejected and we can be (very) confident that the reduction of 4.9 seconds is statistically significant.

Graphical Results:

The Paired T-Test histogram plots the **differences** between the pairs of data.

It shows clearly the average reduction of 4.9 seconds and the confidence interval for this difference (discussed top right).

One Way ANOVA – Overview

ANOVA techniques allow the analysis of averages with three or more samples at a time. The maths is different, but the approach and interpretation of p-values is the same.

Example: A project is looking at the average transaction value between three different sales centres.

The Box plot opposite shows the results of a one month survey at each sales centre, and it looks like there are differences in the average values (the connected dots).

However, the Box plot only has a sample size of 20 for each sales centre, and so you have no idea if the differences between the averages are statistically significant.

The **Analysis of Variance (ANOVA)** method uses a different mathematical approach (see appendix F) to compare the averages of 3 or more samples, but we must still be clear of the hypotheses before applying the technique.

The **Null hypothesis** is: There is **no** difference in average transaction value between the sales centres.

The **Alternative** is therefore: There **is** a difference.

Putting the data into Minitab:
The Minitab menu has two different 'One Way ANOVAs' depending how you have your data prepared:

If all the data is stacked in one column, use:
Minitab: Stat > ANOVA > One-Way

If the data is unstacked in separate columns, use:
Minitab: Stat > ANOVA > One-Way (Unstacked)

One Way ANOVA – Interpreting the Results.

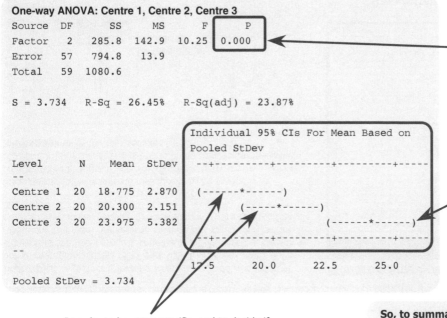

```
One-way ANOVA: Centre 1, Centre 2, Centre 3
Source   DF     SS     MS      F      P
Factor    2   285.8  142.9  10.25  0.000
Error    57   794.8   13.9
Total    59  1080.6

S = 3.734   R-Sq = 26.45%   R-Sq(adj) = 23.87%

                         Individual 95% CIs For Mean Based on
                         Pooled StDev

Level     N    Mean   StDev   --+---------+---------+---------+-----
--
Centre 1  20  18.775  2.870   (------*------)
Centre 2  20  20.300  2.151       (-----*------)
Centre 3  20  23.975  5.382                    (------*------)
--                              --+---------+---------+---------+-----
                                17.5     20.0      22.5      25.0
Pooled StDev = 3.734
```

In order to be more specific, and to decide if Centres 1 & 2 are different, a two sample t-test could be carried out on just these two centres.

 "ANOVA-Sales.mpj"

Session window results:

The p-value on the ANOVA table output is the result for the hypothesis test.

The p-value from this test is 0.000 – which means that we can say (with effectively 100% confidence) that there is a difference in average transaction value between the call centres.

Be careful how you phrase your conclusion: The Alternative hypothesis was that "there is a difference" not "they are all different".

Minitab produces a rough diagram of the sample averages, and their 95% Confidence Intervals.

Centre 3 is the sample with the average value that is most different from the others, and so it is likely to be this centre's results that have caused the p-value of the whole test to be 0.000.

So, to summarise the results in day to day language:
We are very confident that there are some differences in the average transaction value between centres.

Centre 3 appears to be most different from the others, and it has the highest average transaction value, of 23.97 pounds (GBP).

Kruskal-Wallis Test – Overview

The Kruskal-Wallis test compares the medians of different samples of data, and can be used where the data samples are not Normally distributed and do not have any obvious outliers.

Example: A project is looking at the time to deliver different home internet products (ISDN and ADSL). The Box plot below shows that the ISDN product appears to be delivered quicker than ADSL, and the team are keen to validate this conclusion before other tools (such as detailed process mapping) are used to find out why.

Because the ISDN results do not appear to be Normally distributed (a histogram and Box plot have both shown a skewed distribution), a Kruskal-Wallis test is being used to compare the **median** values of the two samples.

Minitab: Stat > Nonparametrics > Kruskal-Wallis

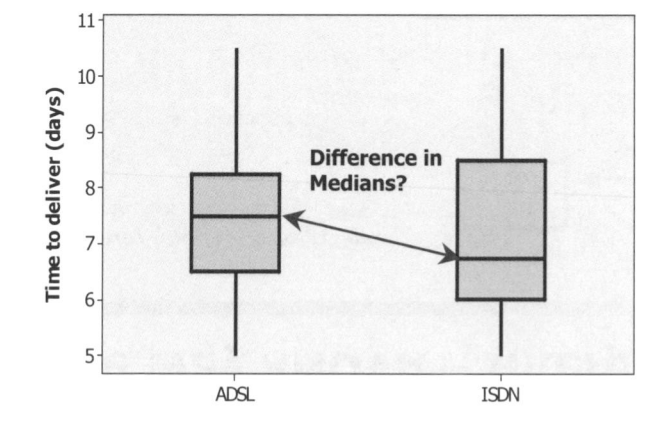

Time to deliver	Product
9	ISDN
6.5	ISDN
7	ISDN
8.5	ISDN
6.5	ADSL
6	ADSL
7.5	ADSL
6.5	ADSL

Data format: Data for the Kruskal-Wallis test must be stacked in one column, with the subgroup code alongside, as shown on the right:

💾 **"Time to Deliver.mpj"**

Kruskal-Wallis Test – Interpreting the Results

```
Kruskal-Wallis Test on Time to deliver

Product    N   Median   Ave Rank      Z
ADSL      25    7.500      29.7     0.73
ISDN      30    6.750      26.6    -0.73
Overall   55               28.0


H = 0.53  DF = 1  P = 0.467
H = 0.54  DF = 1  P = 0.463   (adjusted for ties)
```

Session window results:

Minitab produces only Session window results for this test (no graphical output).

Firstly, the sample sizes and medians of the samples/subgroups are summarised.

The difference in the median values is 0.75 days, but this should be considered alongside the following:

- The size of the samples (25 for ADSL and 30 for ISDN) appears quite low.
- The resolution of the data was to the nearest 0.5 days (see previous page).

For these reasons, a hypothesis test is essential in order to decide if the difference in medians is statistically significant.

Analysing the p-value

The p-value from this test is 0.463. Since this is (a lot) higher than 0.05, we **cannot** say with confidence that there is a difference in the medians of the two samples.

In other words – the medians of the two delivery processes (that the two samples of data represent) **could** be the same as each other.

Note: The two p-values are usually very similar, but if not, use the value that is "adjusted for ties".

So, to summarise the results in day to day language:

Based on the data we have collected, we **cannot** say with confidence that there is a difference between the medians.

The difference of 0.75 hours between the sample medians could easily have occurred just by chance.

If there **is** a difference, more data will have to be collected to prove it.

"Time to Deliver.mpj"

Mood's Median Test – Overview

Mood's Median test compares the medians (central position) of different samples of data, where the samples are not Normally distributed, and where there **are** obvious outliers in the data samples.

Example: A hospital project is looking at the time it takes to process Accident and Emergency (A&E) patients. The data has been stratified into two groups - weekdays and weekends - and the Box plot (below) shows that it appears to take longer to process patients at the weekend.

The team are keen to validate this before they set out to find and understand the root cause of this difference. Mood's Median Test is being used because the weekend data appears to be skewed and also has some outliers (the asterisks).

Minitab: Stat > Nonparametrics > Mood's Median Test

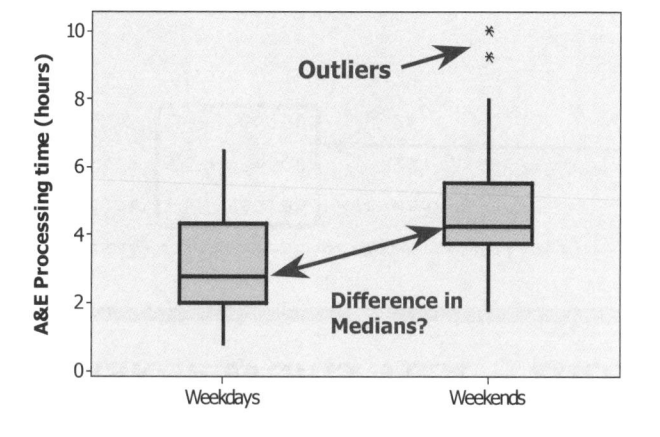

Data format: The data for Mood's Median Test must be stacked in one column with the subgroup code alongside, as shown on the right.

A&E Processing time	Time of week
5	Weekdays
2.75	Weekdays
2.75	Weekdays
4.5	Weekdays
4.5	Weekends
3.75	Weekends
4.25	Weekends

"A&E Processing Times.mpj"

Mood's Median Test – Interpreting the Results

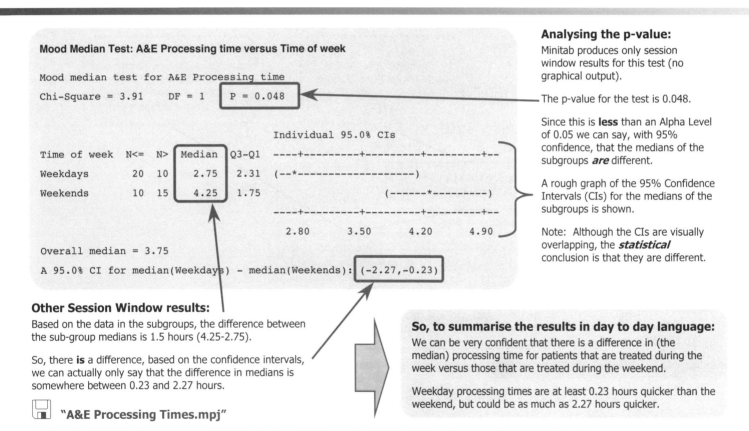

Analysing the p-value:

Minitab produces only session window results for this test (no graphical output).

The p-value for the test is 0.048.

Since this is **less** than an Alpha Level of 0.05 we can say, with 95% confidence, that the medians of the subgroups **are** different.

A rough graph of the 95% Confidence Intervals (CIs) for the medians of the subgroups is shown.

Note: Although the CIs are visually overlapping, the **statistical** conclusion is that they are different.

Mood Median Test: A&E Processing time versus Time of week

```
Mood median test for A&E Processing time
Chi-Square = 3.91    DF = 1    P = 0.048


                                    Individual 95.0% CIs

Time of week   N<=  N>   Median  Q3-Q1  ----+---------+---------+---------+--

Weekdays        20   10   2.75    2.31  (--*-------------------)

Weekends        10   15   4.25    1.75                   (------*---------)
                                        ----+---------+---------+---------+--
                                          2.80      3.50      4.20      4.90

Overall median = 3.75

A 95.0% CI for median(Weekdays) - median(Weekends): (-2.27,-0.23)
```

Other Session Window results:

Based on the data in the subgroups, the difference between the sub-group medians is 1.5 hours (4.25-2.75).

So, there **is** a difference, based on the confidence intervals, we can actually only say that the difference in medians is somewhere between 0.23 and 2.27 hours.

💾 **"A&E Processing Times.mpj"**

So, to summarise the results in day to day language:

We can be very confident that there is a difference in (the median) processing time for patients that are treated during the week versus those that are treated during the weekend.

Weekday processing times are at least 0.23 hours quicker than the weekend, but could be as much as 2.27 hours quicker.

Hypothesis Tests for Variation / Standard Deviation

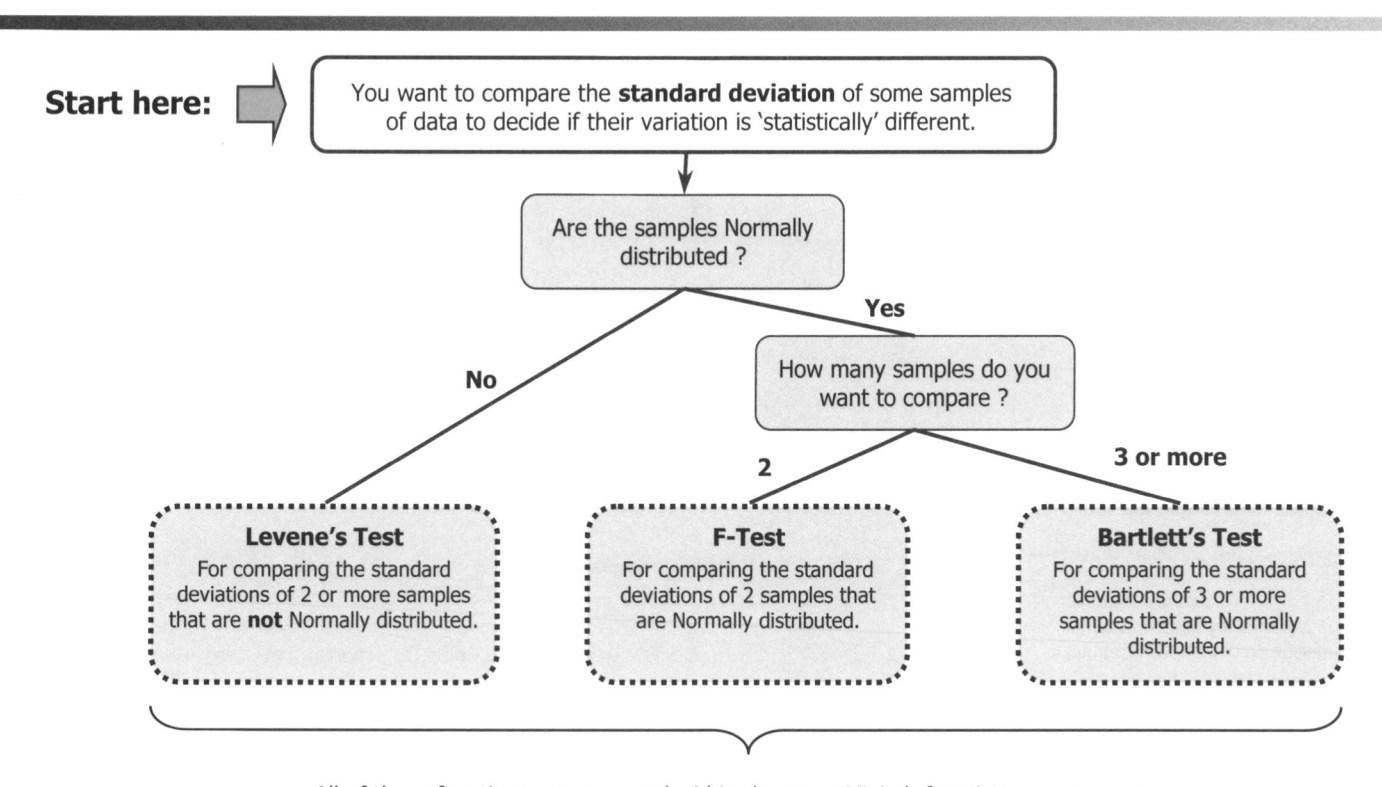

Start here: → You want to compare the **standard deviation** of some samples of data to decide if their variation is 'statistically' different.

Are the samples Normally distributed ?

No

Yes

How many samples do you want to compare ?

2

3 or more

Levene's Test
For comparing the standard deviations of 2 or more samples that are **not** Normally distributed.

F-Test
For comparing the standard deviations of 2 samples that are Normally distributed.

Bartlett's Test
For comparing the standard deviations of 3 or more samples that are Normally distributed.

All of these functions are accessed within the same Minitab function – see next page.

Minitab: Stat > ANOVA > Test for Equal Variances

Test for Equal Variance – Overview

Minitab's Test for Equal Variance provides the results for the F-Test, Levene's and Bartlett's tests.

Example: A project is looking at the time it takes for three different IT Helpdesks to provide an e-mail response to their enquiries.

The Box plot below shows that Helpdesk 3 appears to have a much lower variation than the other two Helpdesks, but a hypothesis test is required to find out if this is statistically significant.

Note that the Helpdesks also appear to have different averages, but a Test for Equal Variance only considers the *range* of the Box plots.

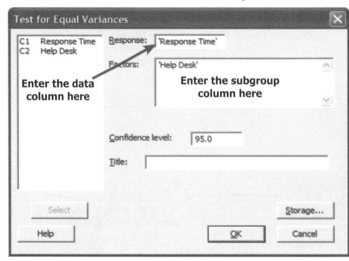

Minitab: Stat > ANOVA > Test for Equal Variances

Data Format: The Test for Equal Variances requires all the data to be stacked in one single column, with a second column that contains the subgroup/sample number.

If your data is in separate columns, you will need to stack it using:

Minitab: Data > Stack > Columns

"Test for Equal Variances.mpj"

Test for Equal Variance – Interpreting the Results

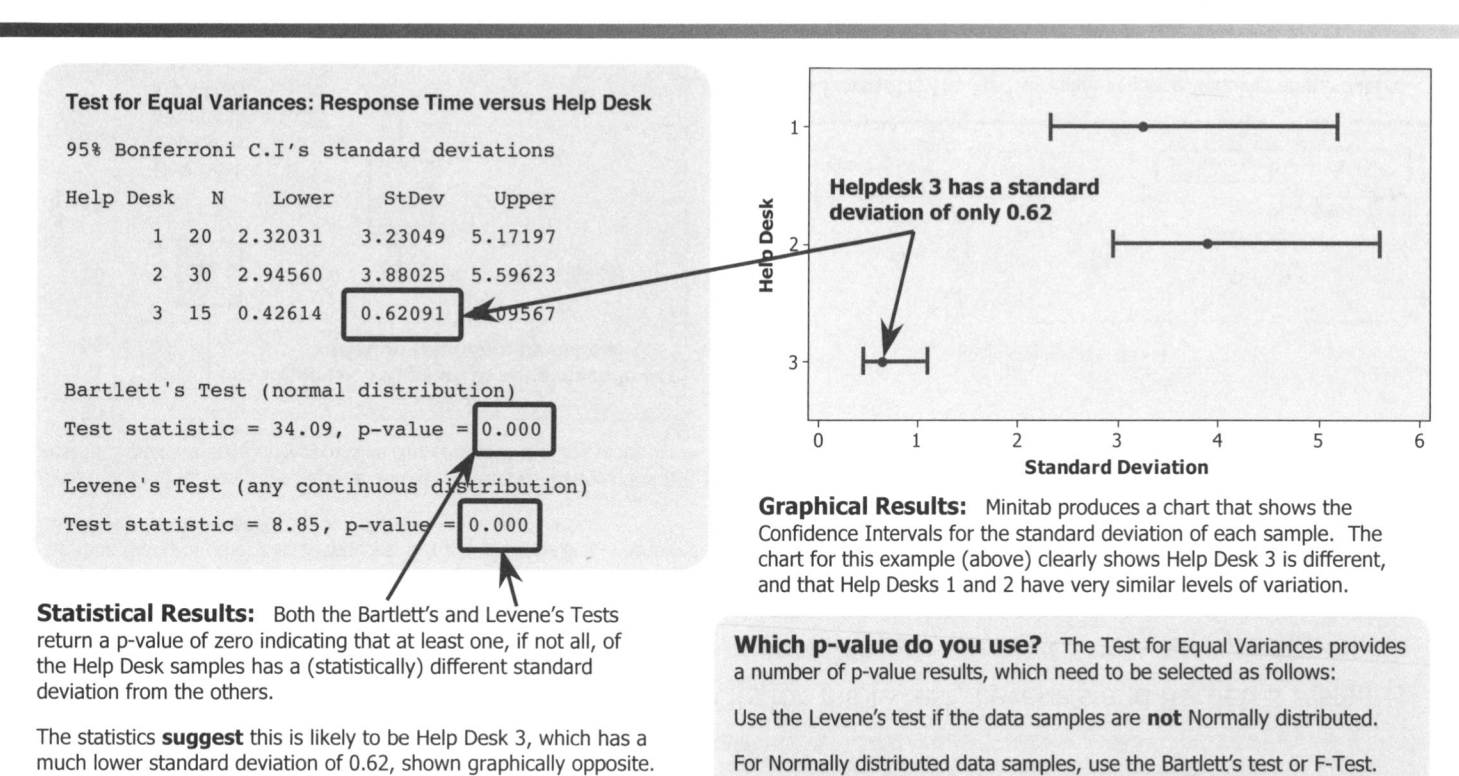

Test for Equal Variances: Response Time versus Help Desk

95% Bonferroni C.I's standard deviations

Help Desk	N	Lower	StDev	Upper
1	20	2.32031	3.23049	5.17197
2	30	2.94560	3.88025	5.59623
3	15	0.42614	0.62091	.09567

Bartlett's Test (normal distribution)

Test statistic = 34.09, p-value = 0.000

Levene's Test (any continuous distribution)

Test statistic = 8.85, p-value = 0.000

Helpdesk 3 has a standard deviation of only 0.62

Graphical Results: Minitab produces a chart that shows the Confidence Intervals for the standard deviation of each sample. The chart for this example (above) clearly shows Help Desk 3 is different, and that Help Desks 1 and 2 have very similar levels of variation.

Statistical Results: Both the Bartlett's and Levene's Tests return a p-value of zero indicating that at least one, if not all, of the Help Desk samples has a (statistically) different standard deviation from the others.

The statistics **suggest** this is likely to be Help Desk 3, which has a much lower standard deviation of 0.62, shown graphically opposite.

"Test for Equal Variances.mpj"

Which p-value do you use? The Test for Equal Variances provides a number of p-value results, which need to be selected as follows:

Use the Levene's test if the data samples are **not** Normally distributed.

For Normally distributed data samples, use the Bartlett's test or F-Test.
(If this example had only two Help Desk samples, Minitab would provide an F-Test automatically, instead of a Bartlett's test.)

Hypothesis Testing for Proportions and Percentages

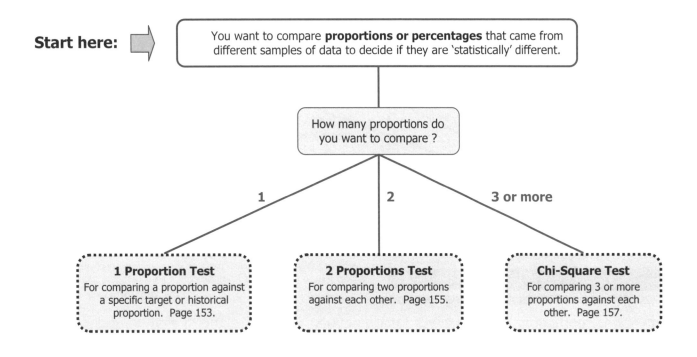

Start here: → You want to compare **proportions or percentages** that came from different samples of data to decide if they are 'statistically' different.

How many proportions do you want to compare ?

1   2   3 or more

1 Proportion Test
For comparing a proportion against a specific target or historical proportion. Page 153.

2 Proportions Test
For comparing two proportions against each other. Page 155.

Chi-Square Test
For comparing 3 or more proportions against each other. Page 157.

1 Proportion Test – Overview

The '1 Proportion test' is similar to the '1 Sample t-test', but is used for proportions & percentages.

What is a 1 Proportion Test?

This hypothesis test compares a proportion (or percentage) from a single sample of data against a known proportion, such as a target or baseline or industry benchmark, in order to decide if they are (statistically) different.

Example: A new wine delivery service has accounted for a 2% breakage rate in its deliveries (the industry average).

However, when they start operating, 4 of the first 100 deliveries are broken when they arrive. Based on this, can they say that their breakage rate is higher than the industry standard? The 'Summarised data' option (opposite) allows the data to be entered directly into Minitab as follows:

The size of the sample (100 deliveries) is entered as the **'Number of trials'**.

The number of breakages (4) is entered as the **'Number of events'**.

Check the Perform Hypothesis Test box (Minitab 15 only), and enter the 2% industry standard under **'Test Proportion'**.

The layout of this input screen has changed for Minitab version 15. Versions 13 and 14 list the number of trials first, then number of events.

Minitab: Stat > Basic Statistics > 1 Proportion

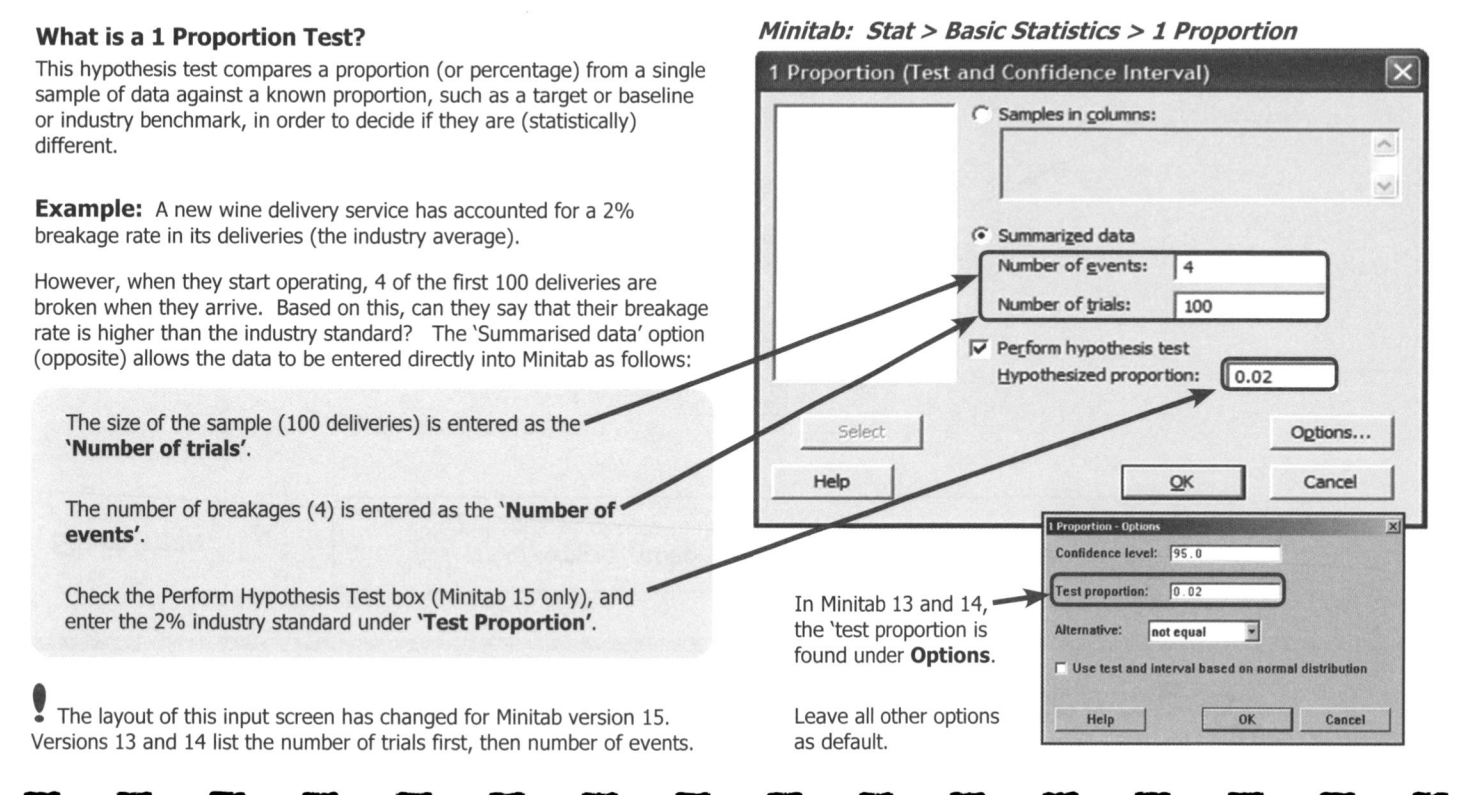

In Minitab 13 and 14, the 'test proportion is found under **Options**.

Leave all other options as default.

1 Proportion Test – Interpreting the Results

There is no graphical output for the 1 Proportion test, just numerical output in the session window.

Test and CI for One Proportion

Test of p = 0.02 vs p not = 0.02

Sample	X	N	Sample p	95% CI	Exact P-Value
1	4	100	0.040000	(0.011004, 0.099257)	0.274

The first line summarises the hypothesis test in shorthand. In this case, in day to day language, this line reads:
"a test for the sample proportion equalling 0.02, versus the sample proportion not equalling 0.02"

Before interpreting the p-value, it's useful to remind yourself what the hypotheses are for the test. In this case:

- The Null Hypothesis is that there is no difference between the proportion from the sample, and the test proportion.

- The Alternative Hypothesis it that there is a difference.

The p-value for this test is 0.274, which is **not** low enough to reject the Null Hypothesis.

This means that we cannot be (statistically) confident, that the sample breakage rate of 4% is different from the industry standard of 2%.

This might seem surprising, particularly given the large sample size of 100. However, remember that because this is Attribute data (yes/no, pass/fail etc) it has quite low resolution, and you therefore need more of it to gain statistical confidence.

95% Confidence Interval for the sample proportion:

A confidence interval for the sample proportion is also given. In this case, the confidence interval indicates that, based on the sample of 4 breakages out of 100, the actual proportion of breakages could be anywhere between 0.011 (1.1%) and 0.099 (9.9%).

Confidence intervals for percentages are discussed in more detail on page 127.

2 Proportion Test – Overview

The '2 Proportion test' is similar to the '2 Sample t-test' but is used for proportions & percentages.

What is a 2 Proportion Test?

This hypothesis test compares two proportions (or percentages) from two different samples against each other, in order to decide if they are (statistically) different.

Example: Two surveys of customer satisfaction have been conducted in two different areas (A & B).

72 out of 80 customers were satisfied in Area A   (90%).
79 out of 100 customers were satisfied in Area B   (79%).

It *appears* that there is a difference and the 2 Proportion Test can be used to validate this statistically.

How to enter the data into Minitab:

The data for a 2 Proportion Test can be entered in several different ways. The first two options are used when you have the raw data in a Minitab file.

The data file below contains the raw data for this example, if you would like to try these.

The '**Summarised data**' option allows the data to be entered directly into Minitab, as shown.

Minitab: Stat > Basic Statistics > 2 Proportion

"**2 Proportion Test.mpj**"

! Note that the **Events** and **Trials** columns have switched places for Minitab version 15.

Options: If in doubt, leave all the Options at their default levels.   The 'Test Difference' should be zero if testing for **any** difference.

2 Proportion Test – Interpreting the Results

There is no graphical output for the 2 Proportion test, just numerical output in the Session window.

```
Test and CI for Two Proportions

Sample   X    N   Sample p
1       72   80   0.900000
2       79  100   0.790000


Difference = p (1) - p (2)
Estimate for difference:  0.11
95% CI for difference:  (0.00658520, 0.213415)
Test for difference = 0 (vs not = 0):  Z = 2.08   P-Value = 0.037
```

Firstly the results for each of the samples are summarised, along with their proportions.

Before interpreting the p-value, it's useful to remind yourself what the hypotheses are. In this case:

The **Null Hypothesis** is that there is **no** difference between the two proportions.

The **Alternative Hypothesis** it that there **is** a difference between the two proportions.

95% Confidence Interval for the difference.

The difference between the two proportions is 0.11 (11%).

However, as with all statistics, we should place a confidence interval around this value, in order to reflect the amount of data in the samples.

The confidence interval says that the difference between the proportions could be anywhere from 0.006 (0.6%) to 0.21 (21%).

This might seem surprisingly wide but remember that Attribute data (yes/no, pass/fail etc.) has less resolution and therefore requires larger samples.

The p-value for this test is 0.037, which is very low (below 0.05) and therefore the Null hypothesis can be rejected.

In other words, we can be (statistically) confident that there is a difference in the customer satisfaction rates of the two samples.

To find out how big that difference might be, see the notes on the 95% Confidence Interval for the difference (left).

Chi-Square Test – Overview

The 'Chi-Square Test' is similar to the '2 Proportion Test' but is used for 3 or more samples.

This hypothesis test is used to compare three or more proportions (or percentages) against each other in order to decide if they are (statistically) different.

Example: Building upon the 2 customer surveys shown in the 2 Proportion Test example on the previous pages, two further customer surveys are conducted (areas C & D) and the results are shown in the table below.

It appears that there might be different proportions of satisfied customers across the four areas surveyed, and a Chi-Square test can be used to validate this statistically.

Minitab: Stat > Tables > Chi Square Test (Table in Worksheet)

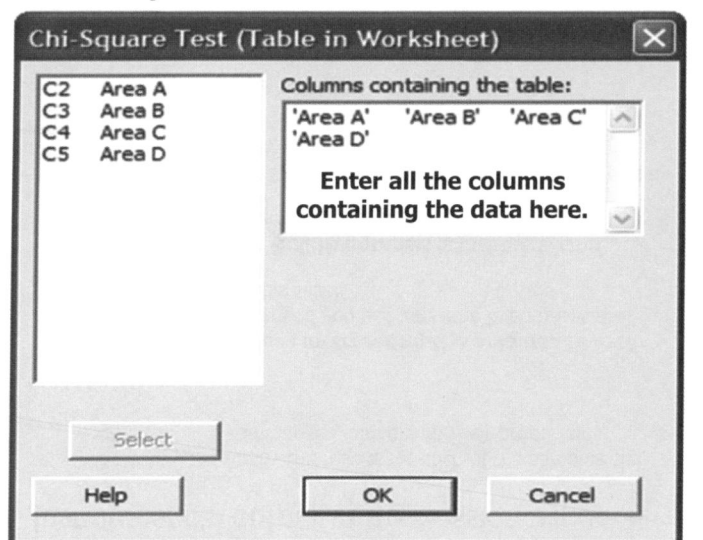

	C1	C2	C3	C4
	Area A	Area B	Area C	Area D
Satisfied	72	79	35	9
Not Satisfied	8	21	15	1

The data for a Chi-Square test is prepared differently from other tests. Enter all the data for the different categories of results but **do not** enter the total sample size. Minitab will calculate the total sample size for each area surveyed, based on the results above.

  "Chi-Square.mpj"

How to enter the data into Minitab:

Data for a Chi-Square test must be presented in a table format as shown on the left. All the columns containing the data are then entered into the Minitab Chi-Square analysis.

Chi-Square Test – Interpreting the Results

There is no graphical output for the Chi-Square test, just numerical output in the session window.

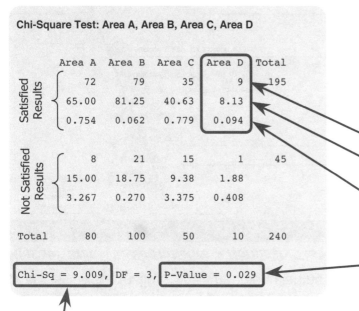

Chi-Square Test: Area A, Area B, Area C, Area D

	Area A	Area B	Area C	Area D	Total
Satisfied Results	72	79	35	9	195
	65.00	81.25	40.63	8.13	
	0.754	0.062	0.779	0.094	
Not Satisfied Results	8	21	15	1	45
	15.00	18.75	9.38	1.88	
	3.267	0.270	3.375	0.408	
Total	80	100	50	10	240

Chi-Sq = 9.009, DF = 3, P-Value = 0.029

The Chi-Square Statistic is the sum of all the Chi-Square values calculated in the table above.

If all the proportions were the same then this Chi-Square statistic would be zero.

How the Chi-Square Test works: The Chi-Square test uses a different mathematical approach, based on the observed and expected results in each category, to decide if there is a statistical difference. However, it still produces a p-value which is analysed and interpreted in the normal way.

For each category of results, such as Area D highlighted here, the Session window shows:

The **observed** number of results in that category

The **expected** number of results for that category (if all the areas had the same level of customer satisfaction).

A **Chi-Square** value which represents the relative difference between the observed and expected results.

The p-value for this test is 0.029, which is very low (and below 0.05) and therefore the Null hypothesis can be rejected.

In other words, we can be (statistically) confident, that at least one, if not all, of the areas surveyed has a (statistically) different customer satisfaction rate from the others.

Anderson Darling Normality Test – Overview

Histograms with Normal curves (p104) and Probability Plots (p107) both provide graphical methods of assessing Normality. The Anderson Darling method provides a Hypothesis Test for Normality.

Minitab: Stat > Basic Statistics > Normality Test

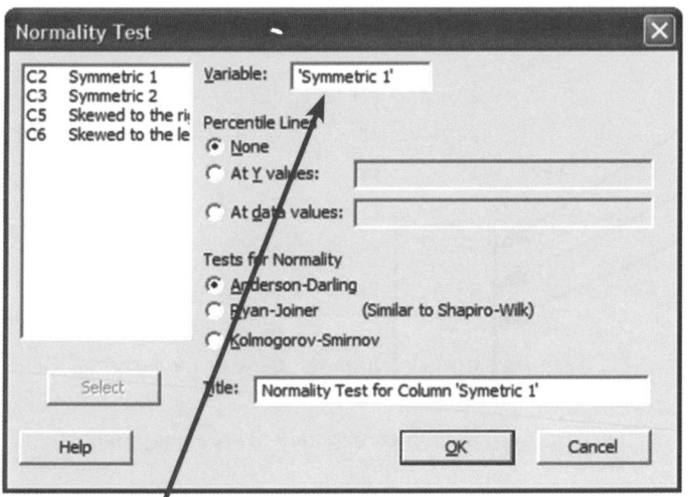

How to enter the data into Minitab:
The single column containing the data is entered under 'Variable', and all other options should be left as standard.

 "Distributions.mpj"

The Anderson Darling Normality Test is slightly different from other hypothesis tests and therefore requires careful interpretation.

The **Null Hypothesis (Ho)** is that the data **is** Normally distributed.

The **Alternative Hypothesis (Ha)** is that the data **is not** Normally distributed.

Whereas often in hypothesis testing we are looking to **disprove** the Null Hypothesis, in the case of Normality testing we are looking to **prove** it.

For this reason, the interpretation of the p-value is the reverse of what we are used to and is as follows for an Alpha Level of 0.05:

If the p-value is less than 0.05, we can be confident that the data is **not** Normally distributed.

If the p-value is greater than 0.05, there is a reasonable chance that it **could** be Normally distributed, and so we usually assume it is.

Where to find the Anderson Darling Normality test:

Minitab's Normality Test function (shown here) produces a Probability Plot (p107) and the p-value for the Normality Test.

Minitab's Graphical Summary (p106) also produces just the p-value result of the Anderson Darling Normality test.

Anderson Darling Normality Test – Interpreting the results

Minitab's Normality Test produces a probability plot with a summary of the data statistics and a p-value for the Anderson Darling Normality Test.

The two examples shown here are taken from the following data file:

💾 **"Distributions.mpj"**

Example 1: This probability plot shows a clearly curved line, which indicates that the data set is almost certainly **not** Normally distributed.

In addition, the Anderson Darling p-value is very low (<0.005) which fits with the probability plot, and means that we can be very confident that the data is **not** Normally distributed.

Example 1:
Data Column C5
'Skewed to Right'

Mean	70.00
StDev	10.00
N	500
AD	46.489
P-Value	<0.005

Mean	50.64
StDev	9.741
N	150
AD	0.632
P-Value	0.098

Example 2:
Data Column C2
'Symmetric 1'

Example 2: This probability plot shows a (relatively) straight line, which indicates that the data may be Normally distributed.

The Anderson Darling p-value (of 0.098) fits the probability plot because it is **above 0.05**, which means that the data **can** be assumed to be Normally distributed.

Individual Distribution Identification – Data Input

So far we have only tested data samples against the Normal distribution. Minitab can also test a data sample against a number of different distributions, in order to find the one that is the best fit.

Minitab: Stat > Quality Tools > Individual Distribution Identification

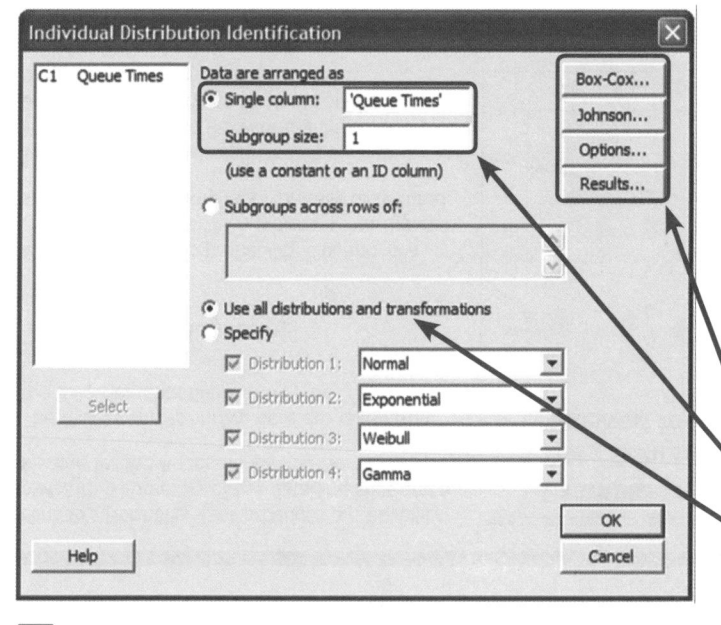

Minitab's Individual Distribution Identification (IDI) function can be used to compare a column of data against a number of different distributions at the same time. The IDI function uses the Anderson Darling method, and provides a p-value output for the fit of the data against each distribution that is being considered.

The resulting p-values are interpreted in the same way as the Normality Test on page 159, as follows:

> **If the p-value is less than 0.05**, we can be confident that the distribution **is not** a good fit for the data.
>
> **If the p-value is greater than 0.05**, then we can assume that the distribution **is** a good fit for the data

If in doubt, leave all four option boxes with their standard default setting for this example.

Enter the column of data to be analysed here and enter a subgroup size of 1 if your data was not collected or sampled in rational subgroups.

For this example, select 'Use all distribution and transformations'. This will compare the data sample against 14 different distributions (and two transformations).

Alternatively, if there is a specific distribution that you want to compare against your data, then select it from one of the drop down lists.

  "Capability–Queue Times.mpj"

Individual Distribution Identification – Data Output

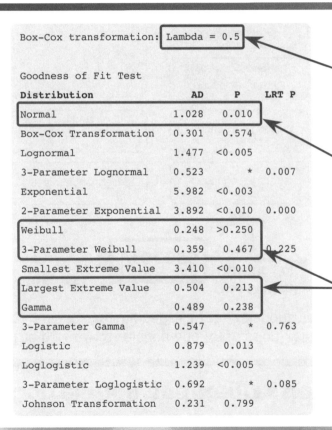

Box-Cox transformation: Lambda = 0.5

Goodness of Fit Test

Distribution	AD	P	LRT P
Normal	1.028	0.010	
Box-Cox Transformation	0.301	0.574	
Lognormal	1.477	<0.005	
3-Parameter Lognormal	0.523	*	0.007
Exponential	5.982	<0.003	
2-Parameter Exponential	3.892	<0.010	0.000
Weibull	0.248	>0.250	
3-Parameter Weibull	0.359	0.467	0.225
Smallest Extreme Value	3.410	<0.010	
Largest Extreme Value	0.504	0.213	
Gamma	0.489	0.238	
3-Parameter Gamma	0.547	*	0.763
Logistic	0.879	0.013	
Loglogistic	1.239	<0.005	
3-Parameter Loglogistic	0.692	*	0.085
Johnson Transformation	0.231	0.799	

Only a portion of the session window output is shown here for interpretation.

Interpreting the Box-Cox Transformation result:

Minitab provides the optimal value of Lambda used in the Box-Cox transformation of the data (see appendix G). In this case, the p-value for the Box Cox transformed data is 0.574, which is above 0.05 and therefore indicates that the transformed data can be assumed to be Normally distributed.

Selecting the distribution that best fits the data sample:

If the Normal distribution p-value is above 0.05 (and is not significantly lower than the p-values for other distributions) then select the Normal distribution as your model, since it provides access to a larger range of analysis tools.

In this case, the p-value of 0.01 indicates that the data is **not** Normally distributed, and you should therefore find an alternative distribution with a higher p-value.

If a number of distributions have close p-values, then select one that you are familiar with, or that will enable you to complete the particular analysis that you require.

In this case, there are four distributions (excluding the transformations) that would provide a reasonable fit for the data (i.e. they have p-values well above 0.05). They are, the Weibull, 3-Parameter Weibull, Largest Extreme Value and Gamma distributions.

Graphical Outputs:

Minitab also produces a probability plot of the data against each distribution, which supports the numerical analysis completed here. As explained on page 107, a straight line on a probability plot indicates that the data fits the distribution in question.

Correlation and Regression Overview

The phrase 'Correlation and Regression' refers to a number of similar tools, all of which can be used to quantify (mathematically) the relationship between process inputs and outputs.

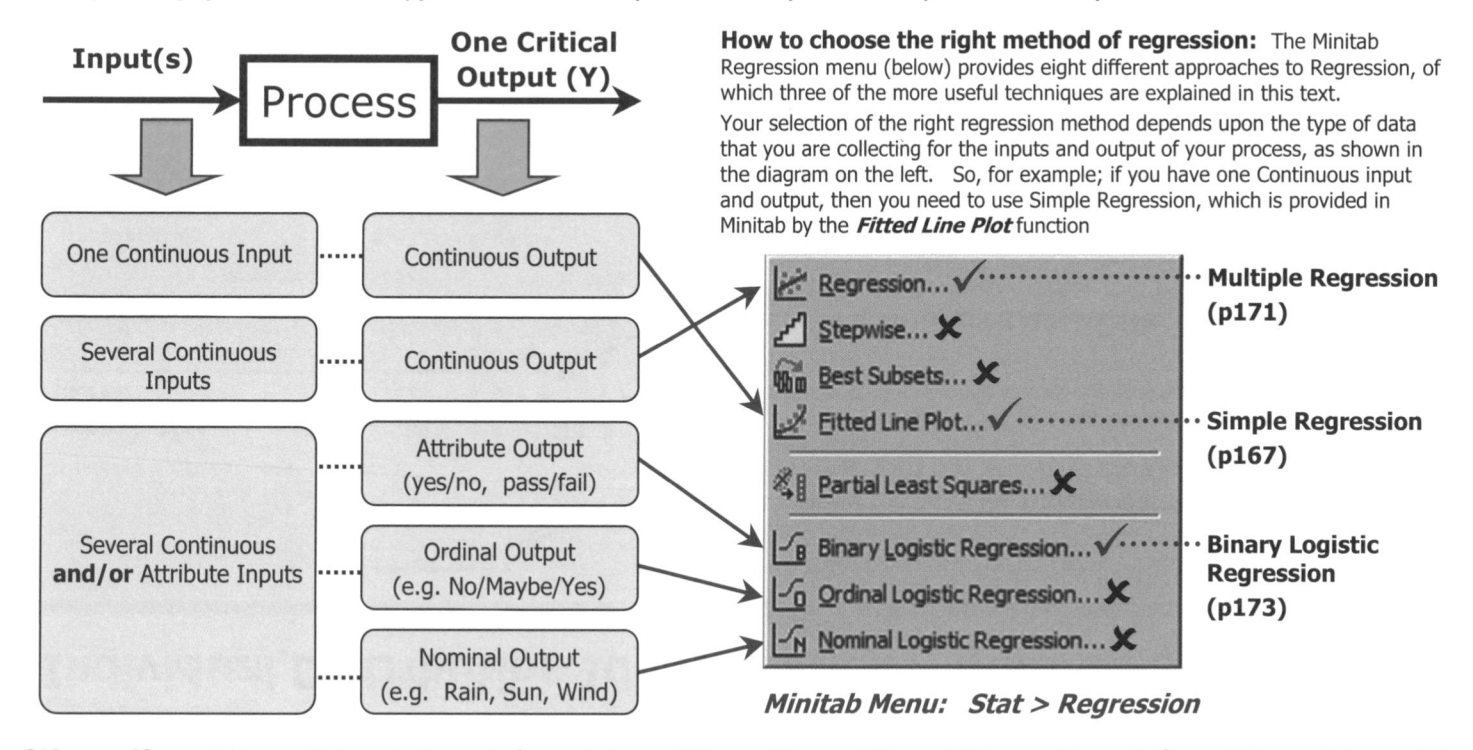

How to choose the right method of regression: The Minitab Regression menu (below) provides eight different approaches to Regression, of which three of the more useful techniques are explained in this text.

Your selection of the right regression method depends upon the type of data that you are collecting for the inputs and output of your process, as shown in the diagram on the left. So, for example; if you have one Continuous input and output, then you need to use Simple Regression, which is provided in Minitab by the **Fitted Line Plot** function

Minitab Menu: Stat > Regression

Correlation and Regression Overview (cont.)

The Regression process	Simple Regression $Y = f(x1)$ The process output (Y) is a function of one process input (x1)	Multiple Regression $Y = f(x1, x2, x3, etc.)$ The process output (Y) is a function of many process inputs (x1, x2, x3 etc.)
Graph the data	Scatter plot (p122)	Matrix plot (p123)
Check for correlations	Use Pearson coefficient (p165)	Use Pearson coefficient (p165), and decide which factors to include in the regression (if in doubt include them)
1st Regression	Simple Linear Regression *Minitab: Fitted Line plot*	Multiple Regression *Minitab: Regression*
Evaluate regression	Check 'R-Squared' Analyse Residuals (p170)	Check 'R-Squared' Analyse Residuals (p170)
Re-run regression if necessary	With different model if necessary (Quadratic or Cubic)	Remove terms that are not significant if necessary
Use the results!!	Control critical process inputs, select best operating levels etc.	

Correlation and the Pearson Coefficient

Once scatter plots have been used to look for correlations the Pearson coefficient can be used to measure the strength of any correlations found.

The Pearson coefficient (r) is used to measure the degree of linear association (correlation) between (Continuous) sets of data. The coefficient ranges from +1 (a strong direct correlation), to zero (no correlation), to -1(a strong inverse correlation), and reflects not only the steepness of the slope but the degree to which the data points are tightly clustered.

Using the scatter plot examples from pages 122/123 (that look at the time to answer calls at a call centre), several Pearson coefficients are shown here alongside the scatter plots they represent.

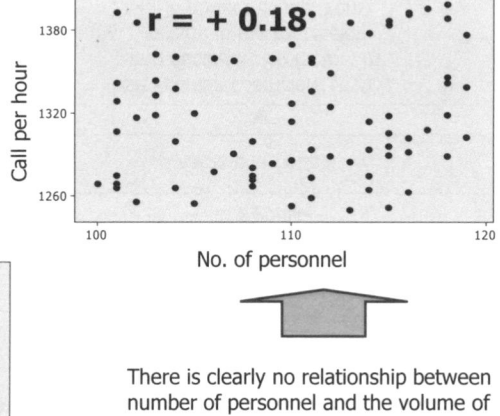

The scatter plot between number of personnel and time per call shows a reasonably strong direct (upwards) relationship, and so the Pearson coefficient is positive and high (0.82). It suggests that the more personnel, the longer they spend on each call.

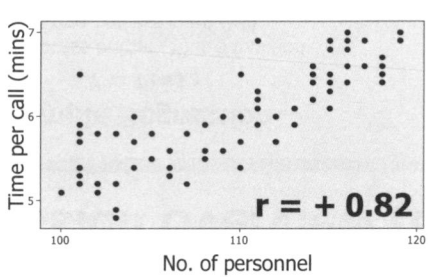

This scatter plot shows a strong inverse (downwards) relationship, and so the Pearson coefficient is very high but negative (-0.98), to reflect the downward slope.

It suggests the more personnel available the quicker the calls are answered.

There is clearly no relationship between number of personnel and the volume of calls received per hour. Accordingly the Pearson coefficient is very low (0.18). Note that it is rare to have exactly zero even when no correlation exists.

Pearson Coefficient – Calculating and Interpreting

The **statistical** significance of your Pearson coefficient must be assessed before you can use it.

Because of the random nature of data, it is possible for a scatter plot to **suggest** a correlation between two factors when in fact none exists.

In particular, this can happen where the scatter plot is based on a small sample size. So, having calculated a Pearson coefficient, we also need to evaluate its statistical significance by considering the sample size it is based on. In other words – is it real?

For this reason, Minitab also calculates a p-value for the Pearson coefficient, based on the Null Hypothesis that there is **no** correlation (see right).

For example, consider the relationship between the number of personnel and the number of calls received (where we know there is actually no correlation). If we had taken a much smaller sample size (say 5), there is a chance that - just by chance - they would have fallen in a way that suggested a correlation (as shown below)...

The Pearson coefficient can be calculated by Minitab, and can be found at:

Minitab: Stat > Correlation

The results are recorded in the Minitab Session window because they are just text output (no graphics).

Interpreting p-values (with 95% confidence):
- **If the p-value is less than 0.05**, then you can be confident that a correlation exists, and use the Pearson coefficient to help quantify it.
- **If the p-value is more than 0.05,** then it's possible that no correlation exists, even if your Pearson coefficient implies one.

r=high

p-value > 0.05

The question is, should we believe it?
The Pearson coefficient is high, but the p-value is also above 0.05, indicating that there might be no correlation.

In this particular case, having collected more data (sample size of 80), the correlation disappears, proving we were right to be suspicious.

Simple Regression

Simple regression is the process of developing a mathematical model that represents your data.

How regression works: The regression process creates a line that best resembles the relationship between the process input and output. As you can see from the scatter plot opposite, it would be impossible to find a line that passes exactly through all of the data points, unless they were on a very specific path.

Instead the best line is found by ensuring the errors between the data points and the line are minimised. In fact, it is the sum of the squares of the errors that is minimised, and so the line is called the **'line of least squares'**.

Different types of mathematical model:

The regression process can fit several different shapes of line, since the linear relationship shown here won't be applicable to all situations. The alternatives are:

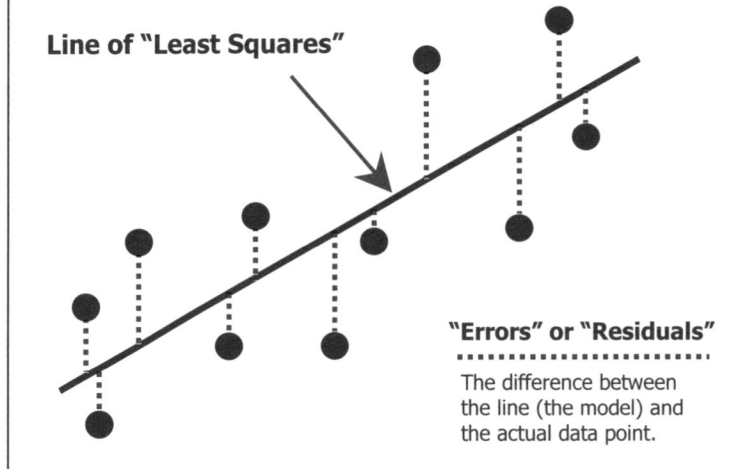

Line of "Least Squares"

Y-axis = Output Variable

"Errors" or "Residuals"

The difference between the line (the model) and the actual data point.

X-axis = Input Variable

Linear: A simple, common relationship that has the simplest mathematical model: $Y = m(x) + c$

(where m and c are constants)

Quadratic: A more complex mathematical model that includes an "x^2" term. This can be used to model process relationships that rise and then fall again.

Cubic: A rarer situation in reality, where the process relationship rises, falls, then rises again (or vice versa).

Residual Errors: Whilst the residual errors between the data and the model are minimised by the 'line of least squares', they remain an indication of how accurately the model will be able to predict the process output. The residuals can be analysed to check that the model line fits the shape of the relationship it is intended to represent, as explained on page 170.

Minitab Fitted Line Plot – Data Input

Fitted Line Plots are the Minitab function for performing simple regression.

The Scatter plot on page 165 suggests a positive correlation between the number of personnel in the call centre and the (average) time spent on each call.

Simple regression can be used to model the relationship between these variables, using Minitab's Fitted Line Plot.

In this case:

■ The Time per Call is the process output (the Response – Y).
■ The Number of personnel is the process input (the Predictor – X).

Type of regression model:
Select the model most appropriate to your data, based on the Scatter plots you have seen. If in doubt start with Linear, and move to a more complex model if the Linear model exhibits problems.

⊞ **"Correlation.mpj"**

Minitab: Stat > Regression > Fitted Line Plot

Graphs: This refers to graphs of the Residual errors from the model – see page 170 for details of analysing residuals.
Selecting 'Regular' residuals (the default) will keep them in the same units as your data.
Check 'Four in one' to see all of the Residuals plots.

Options: Check both 'Display Confidence Interval' and 'Display Prediction Interval' in order to see both the intervals shown overleaf.

Storage: A number of numerical outputs, including Residuals, can be stored in your worksheet for further analysis. Leave this blank until you need them or your worksheet will fill with data very quickly!

Minitab Fitted Line Plots – Data Output

The regression line is placed on a Scatter plot showing the line of best fit that was calculated.

In addition, two further sets of lines are shown:

Prediction Intervals indicate the interval within which you can expect 95% of the process output (data points) to occur.

Confidence Intervals indicate the interval within which you can be 95% confident that the process *average* will occur.

Prediction Intervals

Confidence Intervals

'Number of Personnel' against 'Time per call'

	Regression
	95% CI
	95% PI

S	0.325885
R-Sq	67.1%
R-Sq(adj)	66.7%

The R-Squared (R-Sq) value represents how much of the variation in the process output is accounted for by the model – the closer to 100% the better.

The adjusted version should then be as close to the unadjusted version as possible.

The **regression equation** for this example is:

> **Time per call (Ave.) = - 2.888 + 0.08119 * (No. of Personnel)**

This can be used to predict the average 'time per call' that will be achieved for a specific number of personnel.

The constant 0.08119 is (mathematically) the average increase in Time per call, for an increase of 1 person in the number of personnel.

 "Correlation.mpj"

Using the regression equation: Be careful when using the regression equation to predict process performance. The equation predicts the **average** results from the process, but **individual** results could fall anywhere within the prediction intervals shown.

In addition, you should not use the model beyond the bounds of the data used to create it. In other words, for this example, the model should not be used to predict the Time per call with less than 100 or more than 120 personnel.

Checking the Model – Analysis of Residuals

Confirming that your regression model is a reasonable fit can be done visually with Simple Regression, because you are able to see the Fitted Line Plot. However this is not possible with multiple regression since it is more than two dimensional.

Instead, the residual errors between the model and the data points can be analysed in order to decide if the model is a good fit for the data. This can be done because the behaviour of residuals for a successful model is well established (see the simple linear regression example below).

A model that does fit the data...

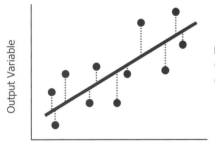

Residuals:
- Normally distributed
- Random

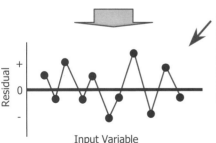

Plotting the residuals of this successful model over the range of the input variable shows them to be random and Normally distributed around zero.

A model that does *not* fit the data well...

Residuals:
- Non-Normal
- Distinctive pattern

The residuals of this 'poorly fitting' model show a distinct pattern, indicating a concern with the model that has been used.

Multiple Regression – Data Input

In reality, the result of a process is rarely a simple relationship with one input variable but instead a more complex result of several factors.

The function of multiple regression is to identify the 'critical X's' (those inputs that have a significant effect on the process), and to mathematically model their relationship with the process output.

To reflect the process thinking employed in Six Sigma you will often hear phrases such as "Y is a function of the process X's", which is written mathematically as:

$$Y = f(x1, \ x2, \ x3, \ etc.)$$

Minitab: _Stat > Regression > Regression_

Answer Time (secs)	Number of personnel	Calls per hour	Time per call (mins)
26	111	1357	6.1
24	114	1265	6.2
27	111	1336	5.9
16	118	1319	6.7
21	115	1290	6.4
22	112	1325	5.7

Process Output / **Input Variables**

💾 **"Correlation.mpj"**

Which input (predictor) variables should you include in the regression?   All of them! – if you think they could be important – but in reality the matrix plots will have given you some clues as to which ones to include.

❗ **The input variables should be independent.**

Because we know that the Time per call and the Number of Personnel are correlated (from the Simple regression on page 169), we should only include one of them in the multiple regression, as shown above.

Multiple Regression – Session Window Output

Extracted from the Session Window:

The regression equation is:

(Average) Answer Time (secs) =

= 246 - 1.98 (Number of personnel) + 0.00180 (Calls per hour-average)

Predictor	Coef	SE Coef	T	P
Constant	245.782	9.335	26.33	0.000
Number of personnel	-1.98338	0.05031	-39.42	0.000
Calls per hour (average)	0.001802	0.006512	0.28	0.783

S = 2.50601   R-Sq = 95.4%   R-Sq(adj) = 95.3%

Analysis of Variance – (results not shown here – see appendix E)

Unusual Observations - (results not shown here)

This regression equation defines the relationship between both the Number of Personnel and Calls per hour (the inputs), and the resulting Answer Time (the output).

Interpreting the equation constants:

- Every extra person produces **a decrease** of 1.98 seconds in the average Answer Time (because it is negative).
- Every extra call per hour produces **an increase** of 0.0018 seconds in the average Answer Time – not very much!

Interpreting the p-values (with 95% confidence):

- **If the p-value is less than 0.05**, then the input variable (predictor) **does** influence the process output.
- **If the p–value is more than 0.05**, then the input variable (predictor) **does not** influence the process output.

So, for this example;
- the Number of personnel (p=0.000) effects Answer Time; &
- the Volume of Calls per hour (p=0.783) does not.

The **R-Squared** value indicates that the input variables in the regression account for 95.4% of the variation in the Answer Time, so it appears that we have found the most important input factors to the process.

However, since the Calls per hour is not significant (see p-values explanation opposite), it must be just the Number of Personnel that is creating all the variation in the Answer Time.

In summary: It is always important to summarise the findings from statistical analysis in day to day language, such as:

- The number of personnel has a dramatic effect on the average Time to answer. It **decreases** by around 2 seconds for each extra person added to the shift.
- The number of incoming calls per hour appears to have little effect on Time to answer or the Time per call.

Binary Logistic Regression – Input

Sometimes the output of the process is measured in Attribute data such as Pass/Fail or Yes/No. This requires a completely different regression approach, called **_Binary Logistic_** Regression.

Example: A project is looking at whether the Quality Approval status (of a call centre) and the average Wrap Up Time (per call) are critical inputs in generating Customer Satisfaction (the process output) across a number of call centres. In this case, customer satisfaction has been measured (in a customer survey) as just Low or High, and so we need to use Binary Logistic Regression.

Minitab: Stat > Regression > Binary Logistic Regression

	Attribute and Continuous Inputs	Attribute Output
Quality Approved?	Average Wrap Up Time (seconds)	Customer Satisfaction
No	190	Low
No	195	Low
No	138	Low
Yes	160	High
No	155	Low

Enter the Binary (Attribute) output here.

Enter **all** of the process inputs to be included in the regression here.
(These can be Attribute or Continuous)

Enter (again) any of the inputs that are Attribute data under Factors.

In this case, enter 'Quality Approved' because this factor has just two levels.

 "Binary Logistic Regression.mpj"

Binary Logistic Regression – Input Options

Options:

Reference Options: This enables you to specify the output result that you would like Minitab to treat as the reference 'event'.

If you don't specify a reference event, Minitab will select the **last** value alphabetically by default.

In this case, our two results are **Low** and **High**. We are happy to have **Low** as the reference event, and so you don't need to enter anything, because Low is after High alphabetically and will be chosen by default.

Reference factor level: This enables you to specify the reference level for any Attribute input factors.

In this case, the *Quality Approved* status is the only Attribute input factor, and by default Minitab will select the first value in that column alphabetically, which is 'No'.

We have shown here how to override the default (by entering the Column followed by the reference value), but in this case it will make no difference, because 'No' is the default anyway.

❗ Use single speech marks like 'this' when entering text into Minitab commands. If you use double speech marks like "this", Minitab will not understand the instruction.

Results: Select the third option, which provides the results that are explained in this text.

Graphs: Select Delta Chi-Square versus probability and versus Leverage for this example.

Binary Logistic Regression – Session Window Output

```
Variable            Value   Count
Customer Satisfaction  Low     70   (Event)
                    High    22
                    Total   92

Factor Information
Factor            Levels  Values
Quality Approved     2   No, Yes
```

Firstly the session window summarises the output and input values.

Here, **Low** Customer Satisfaction is defined as the reference 'event' (i.e. the norm), and it occurred 70 times out of a total of 92 results.

As we know from the raw data, there are two levels of Quality Approved – Yes and No. Minitab confirms the reference value (No) by listing it first.

Interpreting the Logistic Regression Table: The p-values for both inputs are less than 0.05, indicating that we can be confident that both Quality Approved status and Wrap Up Times have a statistically significant effect on Customer Satisfaction.

```
Logistic Regression Table
                                                          95%
                                                 Odds    CI
Predictor                Coef    SE Coef     Z     P   Ratio  Lower  Upper
Constant              -1.98717   1.67930  -1.18  0.237
Quality Approved
 Yes                  -1.19297   0.552980  -2.16  0.031  0.30   0.10   0.90
Avg Wrap Up Time (secs) 0.0250226 0.0122551  2.04  0.041  1.03   1.00   1.05

Log-Likelihood = -46.820
Test that all slopes are zero: G = 7.574, DF = 2, P-Value = 0.023

Goodness-of-Fit Tests
Method             Chi-Square  DF      P
Pearson             40.8477    47   0.724
Deviance            51.2008    47   0.312
Hosmer-Lemeshow      4.7451     8   0.784
Brown:
General Alternative   0.9051     2   0.636
Symmetric Alternative 0.4627     1   0.496
```

So, now that we know they are significant, we should look to the Coefficients to understand the relationships.

The coefficient of −1.192 for Quality Approval indicates that call centres that are Quality Approved tend to have higher customer satisfaction.

The coefficient is negative to indicate that as Quality Approval changes from **No** to **Yes**, Customer Satisfaction tends to move **away** from the reference (Low) to High.

The Odds Ratio of 0.30 indicates that, all other things being equal, the odds of a Quality Approved call centre having Low Customer Satisfaction are 30% of the odds of a Non-Quality Approved call centre having Low Customer Satisfaction.

The coefficient of 0.025 for Average Wrap Up Time indicates that as Wrap Up times increase, the chances of lower Customer Satisfaction increase.

Interpreting the Goodness-of-Fit Tests: See next page.

Binary Logistic Regression – Graphical Output

Interpreting the Goodness of Fit Tests (previous page):

These tests are used to check that the regression model is a reasonable fit for the data. We **do not** want the tests to reject the model (as a good fit), and therefore we are looking for p-values **greater** than 0.05.

In this example, all the p-values are above 0.05, indicating that we can assume that the model is a reasonable fit.

Interpreting the Graphical Output:

For this example, we selected Delta Chi-Square versus probability and versus Leverage under the graph options.

This text does not go into the detail of the calculation and significance of the Delta Chi-Square statistic. However, in broad terms, a high Delta Chi-Square result represents a result that is not fitted well by the model.

In this case, both graphs indicate two data points that have high Delta Chi-Square results and do not appear to fall with the remainder of the data. Using Minitab's Brushing function, these data points can be identified as row numbers 31 and 66 in the data worksheet.

Investigating these two numbers explains why they stand out on the Delta Chi-Square graphs. Both of these data points come from call centres that have no Quality Approval and relatively low Wrap Up times, and yet still have high customer satisfaction. They do not fit the overall model suggested by the regression equation.

The data file for this example (BinaryLogisticRegression.mpj) is based upon data from a Minitab data file (EXH_REGR.MTW).

Design of Experiments (DOE) Overview

This text contains only an overview of the DOE approach since it is a large subject area in its own right and requires detailed understanding before it can be applied with statistical validity. Any reader wishing to use DOE is recommended to consult a specialist text or training event for further advice.

What is Design of Experiments (DOE)?

DOE is the acronym given to a range of experimental techniques in which the process is 'experimented on' in a controlled manner, and the results observed and analysed.

The aim is to identify the important inputs to the process (critical X's) and to understand their affect on the process output.

The maths behind DOE is similar to that for Regression.

What's the difference between Regression and DOE?

▪ Regression techniques are generally used to analyse **historical** data that is taken from the process in its 'normal mode'.

▪ Designed Experiments are used to create and analyse **real time** data that is taken from the process in an 'experimental mode'.

Where is DOE used?

Designed Experiments are more prevalent in Six Sigma projects that are technically orientated (manufacturing etc.) since this environment tends to have processes that can be modified and adjusted in a controlled 'real time' manner.

The principles **are** relevant to transactional projects but the ability to control an experiment in an office environment tends to be limited, and so the application is less frequent.

An example: A project is looking at controlling the thickness of steel emerging from the rolling process shown below. There are lots of input factors (original thickness, roller pressure, roller speed, steel temperature) that can affect the output thickness and an experiment is planned to find out which ones are most important, and to quantify their affect.

What approach would you take to understand this process?

A common approach to experimentation is to only change one factor at a time. So, firstly change the roller pressure, then steel temperature etc.

This can be very time consuming, therefore very costly, and also this approach does not allow for interactions between the process inputs.

DOE provides a range of efficient structured experiments that enable all the factors to be investigated at the same time, with a minimum of trials.

2-Level Full Factorial Designs

A '2-Level Full Factorial Design' is the basic building block of Designed Experiments (DOE).

What is a 2-Level Full Factorial Design?

- **Factorial** means that the input factors are changed simultaneously during the experiment.
- **2-Level** means that every input factor is set at 2 different levels during the experiment; high and low.
- **Full** means that every possible combination of the input factors (at their 2 levels) is used during the experiment.

Example: The '2-level Full Factorial' experiment for the steel rolling process introduced on the page above is shown here on the right.

Each row represents one 'trial' that will be run during the experiment. Because there are three input factors, each set at two different levels, there are eight trials in total.

Standard Order	Run Order	Original Thickness	Steel Temperature	Roller Pressure	Output Thickness
1	2	Low	Low	Low	?
2	7	High	Low	Low	?
3	3	Low	High	Low	?
4	4	High	High	Low	?
5	6	Low	Low	High	?
6	5	High	Low	High	?
7	1	Low	High	High	?
8	8	High	High	High	?

Setting the two levels for each input factor:

The values of the low and high levels for each factor should be chosen with care. Whilst they should be different enough to produce a measurable change in the output (if applicable) they should not be set outside of the normal operating range of the process.

 "DOE-Steel.mpj"

Running an experiment:

The experiment above is shown in its **standard order,** which shows a structured pattern for each input factor.

The **run order** (second column) provides a random sequence in which the experiment should be completed, in order that the results are statistically valid.

DOE Notation in Minitab:

The experiment above is shown using the notation **"low/high"** .

Minitab uses an alternative notation of **"-1 and 1"** but the pattern will be the same.

Optimising Your Designed Experiment

Using the 'Full Factorial Design' as a starting point, the experiment can be optimised for its application.

The downfall of the 'Full Factorial Design' introduced on the previous page is that the size of the experiment doubles for every additional input factor that is included in the experiment. So...

Four input factors would require 16 trials;

Five input factors would require 32 trials; and so on.

Fractional Factorial Designs: The size of an experiment can be reduced by selecting a (carefully chosen) fraction of the trials. The 'fractional factorial' version of the steel rolling experiment is contained within the first 4 rows (versus the normal 8) of the experiment shown here on the right.

Of course, there has to be a trade off for having fewer trials, which is that the **resolution** of the experiment will be reduced. This means that some of the interactions will not be visible, because they will be **confounded** with other effects. However, if this reduced resolution is understood and managed, fractional factorial experiments can be an effective tool.

	Standard Order	Run Order	Original Thickness	Steel Temp.	Roller Pressure	Output Thickness
Fractional Factorial	1	3	Low	Low	High	?
	2	1	High	Low	Low	?
	3	4	Low	High	Low	?
	4	2	High	High	High	?
Replication	5	6	Low	Low	High	?
	6	7	High	Low	Low	?
	7	8	Low	High	Low	?
	8	5	High	High	High	?
	9	9	Mid	Mid	Mid	?

Replication: Factorial Designs only run each trial once, so the sample size for each trial is 1. In order to gain statistical confidence an experiment can be replicated, which means that the entire experiment is repeated. It makes sense that if the results are similar, then statistical confidence is increased.

The design on the right shows one complete 'replication' of the fractional factorial design above it.

Centre Points: Because factorial experiments only study the results of a process at two levels (high and low), they cannot detect if the process output behaves in a linear manner between the two extremes. The use of a **centre point** (trial number 9 above) can be used to detect non-linear effects. Note that the each input factor is set at a 'Mid' level for the centre point trial.

Minitab's Design of Experiments

Minitab: Stat > DOE > Factorial > Create Factorial Design > Display Available Designs

As explained on the page above, the options for 'optimising' an experiment means that there are endless permutations for any one experiment.   Choosing the right combination depends on the specific environment, which inevitably means that experience is a key factor. To summarise:

▪ **Fractional factorials** can be used to reduce the size of an experiment, but the resolution decreases at the same time.

▪ **Replications** can be used to introduce statistical significance to an experiment, but the size of the experiment (number of trials) increases.

▪ **Centre Points** can be used check for non-linear relationships, but require additional trials with the input factors set at "mid" levels.

Minitab's DOE function contains a useful summary of the available factorial designs, shown here on the left.

For any specific number of (input) factors, each completed box below it represents an experiment.   For example:

▪ For 5 input factors, a Full factorial experiment would require 32 trials.
▪ This can be reduced to 16 trials, but the resolution level of the experiment drops to five (V).
▪ The number of trials can be reduced further to 8, but the resolution drops to three, which is potentially unacceptable.

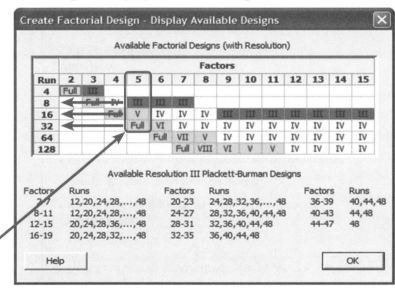

Resolution three is the lowest level available. These 'resolution three' designs require careful application, but can be useful to **screen** for important input factors, which can then be experimented on in more detail.

For example, the chart above shows a 'resolution three' experiment for 7 factors, which requires only 8 runs. A second, more focussed experiment would then usually be required.

Analyse – Checklist

Process Door:
❑ Has the process been mapped in detail (and as it really is)?
❑ Have the team gained first hand experience of the product or process in question?
❑ Have the key types of (or reasons for) failure been identified?
❑ Has Failure Mode Effect Analysis (FMEA) been used (if applicable) to identify the greatest areas of risk in the process/product?
❑ Have brainstorming/5 why's/fishbone diagrams been used to identify possible root causes?

Data Door:
❑ Has the data been analysed graphically to investigate the clues contained within it?
❑ Has the data been stratified where possible to look for clues and benchmarking opportunities?
❑ Have hypothesis tests been used (where applicable) to verify observations made from the graphical analysis?
❑ Have correlation and regression techniques been used (where applicable) to understand and quantify the relationships between the critical process inputs and outputs?
❑ Have designed experiments (DOE) been used (where applicable) to find the critical process inputs?

Finally
❑ Are you confident that you know the true root causes that produce the majority of your process failures?

Analyse – Review Questions

▪ What were your 'theories' about the cause of the problem when you started the Analyse phase?

▪ Were those theories proven during the analysis?

Process Door:
▪ How was the process mapping done? Who was involved?

▪ How did the team get to know the process?

▪ What are the key ways in which the process or product fails?

▪ If an FMEA was completed, what risks were identified for reduction?

▪ Who was involved with the brainstorming/fishbone diagram activities?

Data Door:
▪ What graphs were used for analysing the data? Why?

▪ In what ways was the data stratified?

▪ What (if any) hypothesis tests were used? Why?

▪ If Designed Experiments were used, what process inputs were investigated?   How was the experiment conducted?

Finally:
▪ What are the key root causes of failure or critical inputs to the process?

Overview of Improve

The Improve phase aims to develop, select and implement the best solutions, with controlled risks. The effects of the solutions are then measured with the KPIs developed during the Measure phase.

The flow through Improve:

Generate potential solutions	Select the best solutions	Assess the risks	Pilot and implement
What are all the different possible solutions?	Which solutions are most likely to work?	What are the risks of implementing the solutions?	When, where & how will the solution be implemented?

THE TOOLS AND TECHNIQUES FOR IMPROVE

Negative Brainstorming (p183)
Assumption Busting (p183)
Error Proofing & Benchmarking (p184)
Chain Letters & Billboards (p185)
Brainstorming (p96)
SCAMPER (p186)

Assessment Criteria (p187)
Paired Comparisons (p188)
Prioritisation Matrix (p189)
Pugh Matrix (p190)
Solution Screening (p191)

Fishbone Diagram (p97)
FMEA (p100)

Pilot Studies (p191)

How is the success of the Improve phase measured?   During the Analyse and Improve phases, the data collection systems developed in Measure should remain in place, with the KPI charts being updated regularly and reviewed at the beginning of each project team meeting.

The success of the improve phase is **not** based upon the successful implementation of the selected solutions, but instead when the process measurement (KPIs) have improved and this has been validated with appropriate statistical techniques (graphs, hypothesis testing etc.).

Negative Brainstorming

Assumption Busting

Negative brainstorming helps a team think very differently about a problem, and how to solve it.

Assumption Busting forces you to recognise the underlying assumptions that limit your thinking.

The idea of negative brainstorming:

The concept behind negative brainstorming is that if you can deliberately create a bad product or service, then you probably understand the root causes of the problem that you are trying to solve.

In addition, if you can come up with some ideas for deliberately **creating** a problem, then you can reverse them to develop solutions that **prevent** the problem.

How to use Negative Brainstorming:

Instead of asking your project team how best to **solve** the problem, ask them how best to **create** the problem. So;

Instead of asking "how can we increase customer retention?", ask "how can we make sure we lose all of our customers?"

And instead of "how can we make a 100% perfect products?", ask "how can we make sure we have a faulty product?"

You can facilitate a Negative Brainstorming in much the same way that you would a normal brainstorming event. However, at the end, you must work with the team to reverse the suggestions and convert them into realistic solutions.

Generating solutions is often inhibited by a set of assumptions that may no longer be valid or reasonable. Assumption Busting is an approach for identifying and challenging these assumptions (or rules and procedures).

It's particularly useful when your project team are having trouble thinking 'outside of the box' or have run out of ideas.

The Assumption Busting process:

1) Write down all of your assumptions. Ask yourself; what are the implicit limits that I have never normally challenged?

2) Identify the particular assumptions that are stopping or limiting you solving your current problem.

3) Challenge the assumptions.
The 5 whys technique (page 96) is ideal for challenging assumptions.

Assumption: We cannot despatch products in less than 1 day

Why?   Because the whole process takes at least 30 hours

Why?   Because we can't prepare the shipment until finance has approved the sale and completed their paperwork

Why?   Because the shipping list is produced when finance create the invoice

Why?   Not sure! The shipping list could come straight to use from the sales department who take the order.

Error Proofing

What is error proofing? Error proofing (also known as mistake proofing) refers to the use of solutions and improvements that either;

> • completely prevent or reduce the risk of a failure occurring by eliminating the root cause (preferable)
>
> or
>
> • detect a failure soon after it has occurred.

Error-proofing solutions are particularly suited to repetitive manual tasks that rely on constant vigilance or adjustment.   It is not the use of one, but the application of many 'error-proofing' solutions at every opportunity throughout a product or process, that will reduce the overall long term failure rate.

Examples: Every day examples of error proofing include:
• the use of different size fuel pipes and nozzles on vehicles in order to prevent the wrong fuel being used.
• washing machines will not start or continue turning if the door is opened.
• a warning signal when a car's lights are left on and the door opened (with the engine switched off).

These examples demonstrate that error-proofing solutions work in several different ways. Some **shutdown** the process, others **control** the process to prevent a mistake and others provide a **warning** of a mistake.

Benchmarking

What is benchmarking? Benchmarking is a tool that can be used at several phases of a Six Sigma project.

• In the measure phase, benchmarking involves identifying the best performance attained by similar processes in other organisations and industries. This evidence can be used to help assess if there is the potential to improve the existing process.

• In the Improve phase, benchmarking involves identifying and understanding 'best practices' from other processes and organisations and adapting them to help improve your own process.

How do you benchmark?   Benchmarking is now a common and respected practice in the business world, and accordingly there are many organisations who facilitate and provide benchmarking visits and information. Alternatively, the internet is a valuable (free) source of benchmarking ideas.   Maximum value is usually gained from looking further afield than your direct competitors or industries, since the most innovative ideas and performance can often be found in similar processes that are operating within completely different environments.

Examples:

• A car manufacturer that is looking to provide customised cars to order could benchmark with the pizza delivery or computer industries for ideas on rapid customisation and delivery.

• A supermarket online home delivery service could benchmark with other (non-competing) online retailers for ideas on best practice of website design or effective delivery operations.

Chain Letters

Billboards

What are Chain Letters?

Chain letters are a method of generating ideas and potential solutions. They involve a letter being sent around a specific group of people, with a given objective and timeframe. Each participant is invited to review the previous suggestions and then make modifications, propose alternatives or develop new ideas. Like brainstorming, the aim is to encourage an atmosphere where there are no right or wrong suggestions.

How to use a chain letter:

▪ **Choose an appropriate format:** E-mail is an ideal format for chain letters but you should check that your organisation endorses this use of e-mail! Any format that allows people to view and build upon previous ideas will work.

▪ **Set a time frame and facilitate:** Chain letters succeed through momentum. Set clear timeframes for responding and forwarding the e-mail – a larger volume of "quick/short" responses is often preferable to a few overly detailed suggestions. A chain letter therefore requires some level of facilitation to ensure it is progressing and the responses are focussed.

▪ **Provide a clear objective:** The chain letter should clearly state the objective that is being sought, such as 'providing quicker quotes' or 'keeping the customer better informed'. This helps to generate specific ideas because the participants are focussed on achieving a specific outcome, rather than solving a broad problem.

What are billboards?

Billboards are a similar method of generating ideas and solutions to chain letters. Both methods avoid the use of meetings and aim to tap the creativity of participants in their own time and environment.

Billboards can provide access to a large range of people, but therefore also require careful planning in order that the feedback received is focussed and relevant.

How to use a billboard:

▪ **Prepare:** The location, size and format of the billboard all require careful consideration. Place it where it will be noticed, but also where people will feel comfortable stopping to contribute. Don't forget to provide a pen and paper if required.

▪ **Engage the audience:** The billboard should provide an introduction to what you are doing and why you are asking for suggestions. Always provide some background to the project and ensure that the objective of the billboard is very clear.

▪ **Set a time frame and facilitate:** Billboards are similar to chain letters in that they require momentum to succeed. A billboard that has not changed in 3 months is clearly not part of a very active project!, and will not solicit many useful responses. Set a clear timeframe for removing the billboard and regularly review the feedback being received, updating the board as required.

▪ **Provide feedback:** Once you have collected and made use of the billboard suggestions, don't forget to provide feedback and thank people for contributing.

SCAMPER

SCAMPER is another useful idea generation technique. It provides a checklist that can be used to improve upon an existing design/product/service or to develop new ideas and solutions.

SCAMPER is actually an acronym that provides a framework of challenging questions. It helps you to take a structured approach to developing ideas, and can be used to develop new solutions or refine existing ones.

It's particularly useful towards the end of your 'idea generation' phase, when ideas might be flowing slower and the team need re-invigorating!

How to use SCAMPER:

It is best used by a team, but can still be used individually. Like many of the idea generation tools, if you are working with a team this technique requires good facilitation to be effective.

Good facilitation involves ensuring that you keep the team focused and that everyone has a chance to give input. As a facilitator, try and get the team to build upon other peoples ideas, comments and suggestions in a positive way. This can be done by taking peoples suggestions and turning them around using leading questions such as how? why? why not? when?.

Work systematically and consider each element of a solution/product/service against the key words of SCAMPER in order to develop ideas for improvement.

S **Substitute** – Can you substitute people, components, materials or processes from elsewhere?

C **Combine** – Are there functions, elements, features or processes that you can combine to your advantage?

A **Adapt** – Can you alter or adapt ideas from different processes, products or industries to your advantage?

M **Modify** – Can you modify a feature or function, perhaps by increasing/decreasing it, or changing its shape or attributes?

P **Put to another use** – Can you put your product, service, solution or idea to a different use? Can you access a new market?

E **Eliminate** – What would happen if you removed an element or process? How would you work round it? Would it simplify things?

R **Reverse** – Can you turn things inside out or upside down? What would happen if you did things back to front?

Assessment Criteria – Development and Weighting

Developing agreed assessment criteria is the first step in selecting the best solution for the project.

Assessment criteria provide a constant basis of comparison within the solution selection techniques that are used next, and so it is important to get them right!

It's also important to involve a wide group of people in the development of the assessment criteria, to avoid missing any critical perspectives or having your selected solutions open to challenge later on.

Brainstorming is a good place to start for developing a list of criteria

Some common assessment criteria:

- Will it solve the problem or achieve the objective?

- Will it improve customer satisfaction?

- Will it impact the customer negatively during implementation?

- How easy is it to implement?

- Are there any potential problems or risks?

- What is the cost?

- Does it fit with the strategy of the business?

- Are there any potential regulatory or safety compliance risks

Having agreed the assessment criteria, you then weight them against each other.

There are two key approaches to weighting your assessment criteria:

1) Use the paired comparisons technique described on page 188 to compare and prioritise the different criteria. This technique is usually used to select solutions, but it can be used to weight criteria too.

2) Develop a team consensus using multi-voting, in which you get your team members to apportion 100 points across the potential criteria.

You then total up the scores for each assessment criteria, and this provides a weighting for that criteria (as shown below) for use later on.

Name → Assessment criteria	Nathan	Simon	Melanie	Graeme	Miles	Weighted Totals
Can be implemented quickly	15	10	5	10	5	45
Will solve the problem fully	40	60	35	50	55	240
Costs less than 100K Euros	10	10	20	20	5	65
Won't impact customer	20	15	25	15	30	105
No regulatory risks	15	5	15	5	5	45
	100	100	100	100	100	500

Paired Comparisons (a.k.a Pairwise Ranking)

Paired Comparisons is a team based approach for ranking different options against each other. It is a particularly useful technique where there is little objective data to base a decision on.

Paired Comparisons is most commonly used to rank potential solutions or weight assessment criteria against each other. You need a team of people with knowledge of the process and effective facilitation skills!

How to complete a Paired Comparison:

1) Label the solutions or criteria that you are going to compare by letters (**A**, **B**, **C** etc.).

2) Draw a comparison matrix, such as the one shown opposite.

3) Taking two solutions/criteria at a time, ask the team to compare them against each other and decide which one is better or more important.
NB: To do this for solutions, you will first have to define the criteria against which to make your decision.

4) Write the result (the solution or criteria with the most votes) in the relevant box. So in this case, when comparing solutions A and B, solution B was selected and written in the box.

5) Rank the solutions, or weight the criteria as follows:

- If you are comparing solutions, rank the solutions in order of the number of times they were selected as the best of a pair.

- If you are weighting criteria, then work out the weighting for each criteria, by dividing the number of times it was chosen by the total number of decisions that were made.

Comparison Matrix...

	A	B	C	D	E
A	-	B	A	D	A
B	-	-	B	B	B
C	-	-	-	C	E
D	-	-	-	-	D
E	-	-	-	-	-

For ranking solutions...

B	4	1st
A	2	2nd
D	2	2nd
C	1	3rd
E	1	3rd

For weighting criteria...

B	4/10 =	0.4
A	2/10 =	0.2
D	2/10 =	0.2
C	1/20 =	0.1
E	1/10 =	0.1

Prioritisation (or Solution Selection) Matrix

A Prioritisation Matrix is a structured technique for selecting a solution from several alternatives. It combines the weighted criteria and list of possible solutions that the team have already developed.

A prioritisation matrix helps to weigh up the pros and cons of each possible solution using the weighted criteria and consensus of the team, and so provides a good chance of selecting the most appropriate solution.

How to complete a Prioritisation Matrix:

1) Finalise the selection of solutions that you will include in the matrix. Remove any clear "no-go" solutions – those that the organisation just wouldn't accept at any cost.

2) Re-confirm that the team are happy with the assessment criteria and their weightings that will be used. In addition, you should ensure there is some element of cost to benefit assessment within the criteria.

3) Facilitate the team scoring of the solutions, ensuring that consensus is reached. Calculate the Final Weighted Scores, and Overall Rankings.

4) Reality Check! You should verify that the team are all happy that the solution selected using the Prioritisation Matrix is the right one

Criteria	Can be implemented quickly	Will solve the problem fully	Costs less than €100K	Won't impact customer	No regulatory risks	Final Weighted Score	Overall Ranking
Weighting	0.09	0.48	0.13	0.21	0.09		
Solution A	8	4	8	7	1	5.24	4th
Solution B	8	7	9	6	5	6.96	1st
Solution C	4	9	4	3	7	6.46	2nd
Solution D	4	5	3	10	4	5.61	3rd

Where do the weighting figures come from?

The weightings figures are calculated from the multi-voting system described on page 187. For example, the weighting for the first criteria (which was "*can be implemented quickly*") is calculated as follows:

$$\frac{\text{Weighted Total}}{\text{Total Available}} = \frac{45}{500} = \mathbf{0.09}$$

How are the Final Weighted Scores calculated?

The final scores for each of the solutions is the sum of each individual score multiplied by the weighting for that criteria. For example:

Solution A Final Weighted Score =

$(0.09 * 8) + (0.48 * 4) + (0.13 * 8) + (0.21 * 7) + (0.09 * 1) = \mathbf{5.24}$

Pugh Matrix

A Pugh Matrix is not only a method of **selecting** a solution, but a method for further **developing and refining** the potential solutions together, so that a 'best of all worlds' solution can be found.

The Pugh Matrix works by comparing the different solutions against a chosen 'standard' (in this case Solution C) for each assessment criteria. Further solutions can then be developed by mixing the positive aspects of a number of solutions, as described below:

How to complete a Pugh Matrix exercise:

1) Finalise (with your team) the selection of solutions, assessment criteria and weightings that you will include in your matrix.

2) Choose a solution that will be your 'standard' for comparison.

3) Compare each solution again the standard for each criteria, making a note of whether you think it is better, the same, or worse in that respect.

4) Calculate the Weighted Sums for each solution

5) Focusing on the strongest solutions, look for opportunities to combine the best aspects of different solutions.

6) Re-run the Pugh Matrix again with the new solutions if required.

How to calculate the Weighted Sums:

The Weighted Sum of Positives is calculated by multiplying each positive sign by its weighting, as follows for Solution A: $(1*1) + (1*1) + (1*2) = 4$

The weighted sum of negatives is calculated in a similar method.

Key:
' **+** ' = Better than standard
' **S** ' = Same as standard
' **-** ' = Worse then standard

Criteria	Solution A	Solution B	Solution C	Solution D	Weighting
Can be implemented quickly	+	+	S	S	1
Will solve the problem fully	-	S	S	-	5
Costs less than €100K	+	+	S	S	1
Won't impact the customer	+	+	S	+	2
No regulatory risks	-	-	S	-	1
Weighted Sum of Positives	4	4		0	
Number of 'sames'	0	1		2	
Weighted Sum of Negatives	-6	-1		-6	

Solutions / Ideas

Solution Screening

What is Solution Screening?

Solution screening is a method of checking that the potential solutions developed during the Improve phase still meet the basic requirements of the project goal. It should be used as a final 'sanity check' before selecting the solution(s).

A list of screening criteria are developed that reflect the basic requirements of the project goal, such as:

- Will the solution eliminate the root cause of the problem?
- Is the solution likely to be effective?
- Will the customer accept the solution?
- Will the solution be accepted by the business?
- Is the solution capable of becoming 'business as usual'? (see standardised processes – page 210)

Solution screening is just one of a selection of tools that can be used during the Improve phase to help ensure that the solutions developed will be effective.

Affinity diagrams (p98) and fishbone diagrams (p97) can also be used to help organise and develop the ideas developed from chain letters or billboards (p185). Team voting can then be used to narrow down ideas, with solution screening providing a final check. Finally, pilot studies (opposite) can be used to check the effectiveness of a solution in practice, before full implementation.

Pilot Studies

What is a pilot study?

A pilot study is a localised, controlled trial of a solution in order to test its effectiveness before full implementation. There are many advantages to completing a pilot study, including:

- It validates the effectiveness of the solution.
- It promotes buy-in from key stakeholders.
- The final solution can be optimised (fine tuned) from the lessons learnt during the pilot study.
- Valuable implementation lessons can be learnt during the pilot study and incorporated into the full roll out plan.
- The risks and costs associated with a pilot study (versus full implementation) are low.
- The effectiveness of the solution can be measured, and checked against the goal statement or predicted results.

Planning a pilot study:

- **Where?** The scope and area of the pilot study should be chosen carefully, and be as representative of the wider process as possible.
- **When?** The timeframe of the pilot study must be sufficient for the process to respond to the solutions implemented, and should also be clearly communicated to key stakeholders.
- **How?** A detailed data collection plan must be in place in order to capture the results of the pilot study. The amount of data must also be sufficient to reach statistically valid conclusions (see page 48).

Improve – Checklist

❑ Have alternative improvement ideas been generated for each of the root causes?

❑ Have structured techniques been used to ensure that the alternative improvement ideas are innovative and will create a step change in performance?

❑ Have the improvement ideas been assessed and compared using relevant criteria such as ease, speed, cost, benefit etc.?

❑ Before implementing improvements, have the risks been assessed in a structured way (e.g. FMEA)?

❑ Have the improvements been proven in pilot studies before full implementation (if appropriate)?

❑ Have the improvements been fully implemented and become "business as usual"?

❑ Have the KPIs been monitored, and the performance improved?

❑ Have the improvements in the KPIs been validated graphically and statistically?

Improve – Review Questions

▪ How were the different improvement ideas generated?

▪ Who was involved in this process?

▪ How were the potential improvement ideas assessed and compared?

▪ How were the risks of the various improvement ideas assessed?

▪ Why did you choose your selected improvements?

▪ How much of an improvement is expected from the selected solutions?

▪ Were the solutions piloted before full implementation?
  If so, where?, when?, how?, why? etc.

▪ When was the full implementation? (Is it still ongoing?)

▪ How was the full implementation managed? (Project planning etc.)

▪ Has the process improved? Can we see the KPI charts?

▪ Has the goal statement been achieved?

▪ How are the KPIs being monitored and reviewed?

Blank Page

Overview of Control

The Control phase aims to ensure that the solutions that have been implemented become 'embedded' into the process, so that the improvements will be sustained after the project has been closed.

The flow through Control:

Implement ongoing measurement	Standardise the solutions	Quantify the improvement	Close the project
How will the process be measured after the project?	Have the changes become 'business as usual'?	Has the project goal been achieved?	Ensure the project has a clear closure process

THE TOOLS AND TECHNIQUES FOR CONTROL

Statistical Process Control (SPC) (p159-p208) Control Plans (p209) KPI Trees (p32)	Standardised Processes (p210)	Hypothesis Testing (p128) Statistical Process Control (SPC) (p195-p208)	Project Report (p210) Closure Action Log (p210)

Ongoing measurement of the process: Processes must have rigorous data collection systems in place before a project can be closed. This involves defining who is responsible for collecting and reviewing the data, as well as ensuring that the measurements have been integrated into the organisations KPI trees/dashboards.

Closing projects is a critical element of a successful Six Sigma program. There are often opportunities to apply the lessons learnt from projects to different areas of the business, which requires clear action plans, and a 'knowledge management' approach to documenting projects.

Statistical Process Control – Overview

Statistical Process Control (SPC) charts are essentially a sophisticated form of Time Series plot that enable the stability of the process and the type of variation involved to be understood.

The traditional role of SPC charts is that of a 'real time' process tracking tool in a production environment. In Six Sigma, SPC charts can be used for a much wider range of purposes, and are applicable to all industries.

An example of an SPC chart is shown below. It plots the performance of a process over time and shows control limits (not specification limits) which the results will fall between if the process is stable and 'in-control'.

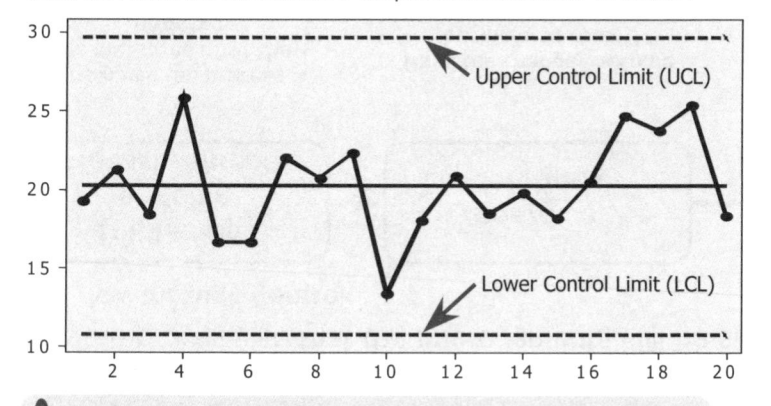

How are SPC charts used? There are two key uses:

1) "Historical Analysis" – the analysis of historical data to assess the stability of the process.

2) "Ongoing Control" – the real time analysis of process performance that aims to detect and react to process changes.

These are explained further on page 198.

What do SPC charts detect?.....　　Changes!
- changes in process average
- changes in process variation
- one off events such as special causes
　　　　(explained further on the next page).

When are SPC charts used? Because of their name, SPC charts are usually placed within the Control phase of Six Sigma. However they are useful throughout the Measure and Analyse phases as well, as explained on page 198.

❗ Deploying SPC charts will not mean that processes will suddenly become 'in-control'. What they can do however, is help you to measure and understand processes, and provide a rigorous approach for deciding when a process has changed and/or needs intervention.

❗ **SPC charts need maintenance!** SPC control limits require regular review in order to make them relevant and meaningful. This in turn requires a Quality Control 'infrastructure' to control the review process.

There are many types of changes that can occur in a process, but they can usually be characterised as one of (or a combination of) the following three different types of change.

Changes in the average...

Time

A change in process average: The time series chart to the left shows a clear increase in the process average.

Whilst this example is visually very obvious, SPC charts can detect much smaller changes that wouldn't normally be obvious to the human eye.

This might represent an uncontrolled change in the process or be the result of a deliberate improvement to the process.

Changes in variation...

Time

A change in process variation: The time series chart to the left shows a clear increase in the amount of variation in the process (note that the average doesn't necessarily change).

Again, this example shows a very marked change, but SPC charts can detect much smaller changes in variation that wouldn't normally be obvious.

One off events (Special Causes): The time series plot to the right appears to be relatively stable (and 'in control' – see process stability on page 72), with the exception of two points that are significantly higher than the rest. These two points are known as special causes because they fall outside of the expected variation range of the process, and are therefore likely to be as a result of a specific 'special cause'.

SPC charts help to detect these special causes, which can then investigated to identify the root cause.

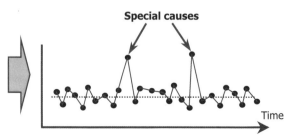

Special causes

Time

How SPC Charts Detect Changes...

As shown in the SPC Routemap on page 199, there are a range of SPC charts to choose from depending on the application and type of data. However, they all work in roughly the same way, as follows:

1. The performance of the process is plotted as a Time Series plot.
2. The level of (historical) variation in the process is assessed.
3. Control limits are drawn on the plot based on the variation measured.
4. Each data point on the chart is then assessed against a number of 'tests' (see below for more detail on the tests).
5. Any data points that fail the tests are highlighted for investigation.

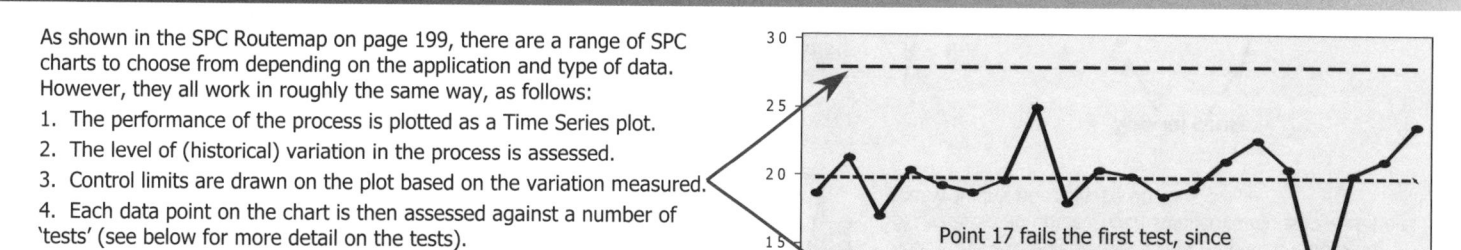

Point 17 fails the first test, since it falls outside the control limits.

SPC Chart Tests are designed so that they are **unlikely** to be broken if the process has **not** changed. Each type of SPC chart has a set of tests (found under Minitab's Options) that are applied to each data point.

There are 8 tests for the 'Individuals' type of SPC chart (above), and the Minitab Options screen that lists the tests is shown here on the left.

The first, most common test is that if any of the data points fall outside of the Control Limits (+/- 3 Standard Deviations) then they are considered to be 'special causes'. Data point 17 on the chart above fails this rule.

The remainder of the tests are more complex, but all of them are designed to detect changes in the process.

Minitab 15 enables the user to customise the tests, by modifying the K values shown here. So, the first test **could** be changed to detect single data points outside of 2 standard deviations from the centre line, by changing the K value to 2. However, for almost all situations, these K values should be left at their default levels shown here.

Where SPC Charts Can Be Used....

For 'Historical Analysis': This approach is often used in the Measure and Analyse phases to understand how the process has been behaving historically. SPC charts can be used to assess whether the process was stable or not, and to assess the type of variation present (common or special cause – page 72) – which both have implications for the type of improvements that will be required to improve the process.

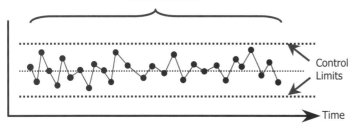

In this case, the control limits are set up based upon **all** the data points that are in the chart (i.e. all the historical data).

For 'Ongoing Control': Once the process has been improved, the Control phase aims to ensure the new process data is reviewed on an ongoing basis to check that the process performance does not deteriorate again. SPC charts can be used for this purpose since they provide a clear indication of when the process has or has not changed.

In this case the control limits are set up based upon the **new process** data that you have, and are extrapolated forward. Each future result is then assessed against those control limits.

All of the different types of SPC charts described on the subsequent pages have the ability to be used both for 'historical analysis' or for 'ongoing control'. If required for "ongoing control", the statistics of the new process data are entered into Minitab (as an average or standard deviation for example) and Minitab then sets up the future control limits based on this data.

Statistical Process Control Routemap

The selection of an appropriate SPC chart is based upon the type of data (world) that is available.

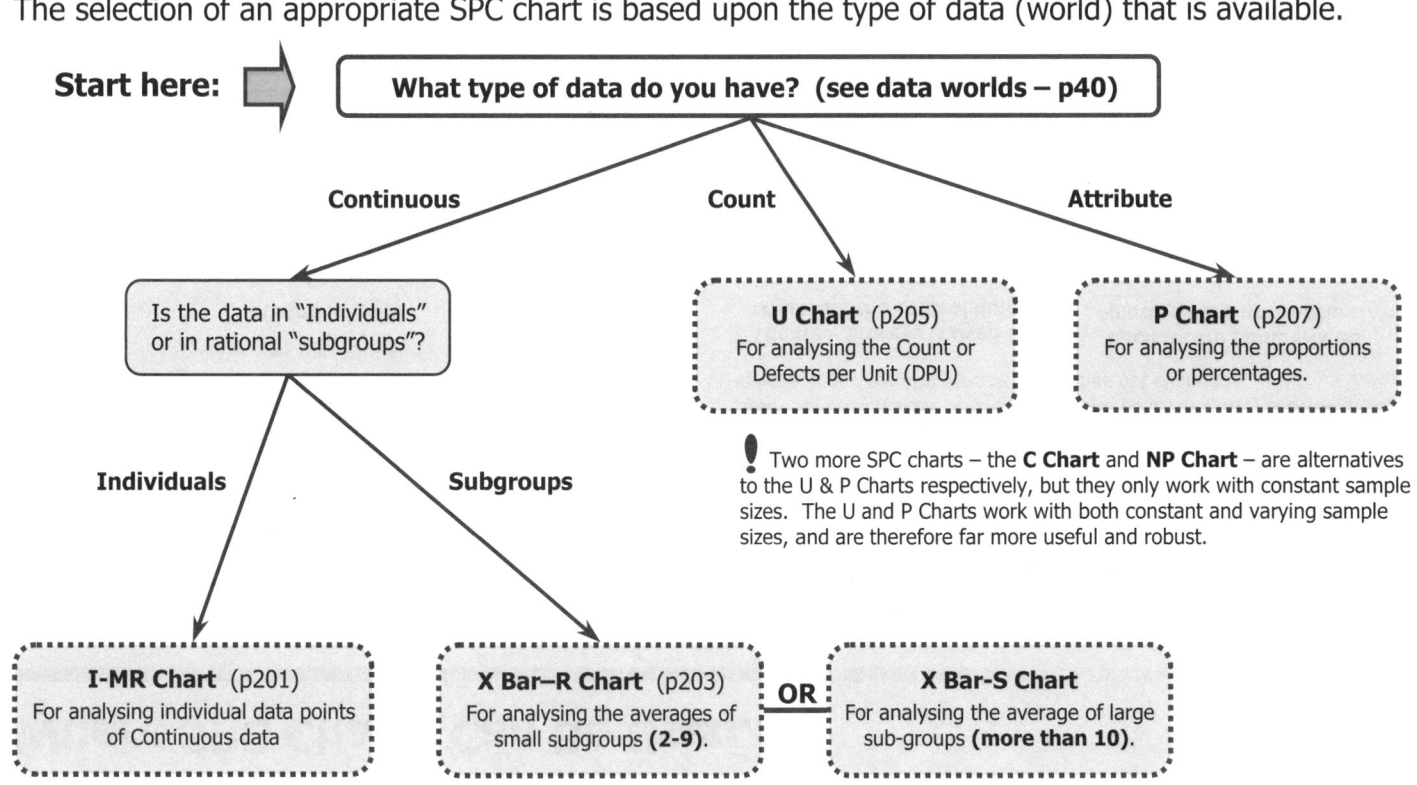

Blank Page

I-MR Chart (Individual – Moving Range) – Input

I-MR Charts are for use with Continuous data that does not have any rational subgroups. In other words, all the data points should have been collected individually.

❗ **I-MR Charts** work best with data that is Normally distributed. If your data is Non-Normal, then the I-MR chart may produce invalid results because some of the tests will be failed when they should not be. You could try using a XBar-R Chart, which works with Non-Normal data because it plots averages, not individual data points.

Example: A building materials company is investigating the amount of sand its filling process puts into each bag. A data file containing the historical data of 50 bags is available to help understand if the process is 'in-control' or 'stable'.

The **Scale, Labels** and **Multiple Graphs** functions all contain self explanatory options for the formatting of your graphs and are normally left as default.

Data Options allows you to use only a specific set of rows from your data in the I-MR chart.

I-MR Options contains several important settings that control how the I-MR is completed. The two most commonly used, **parameters** and **tests** are described in more detail here.

 "SPC-I-MR.mpj"

Minitab: Stat > Control Charts > Variable Charts for Individuals > I-MR

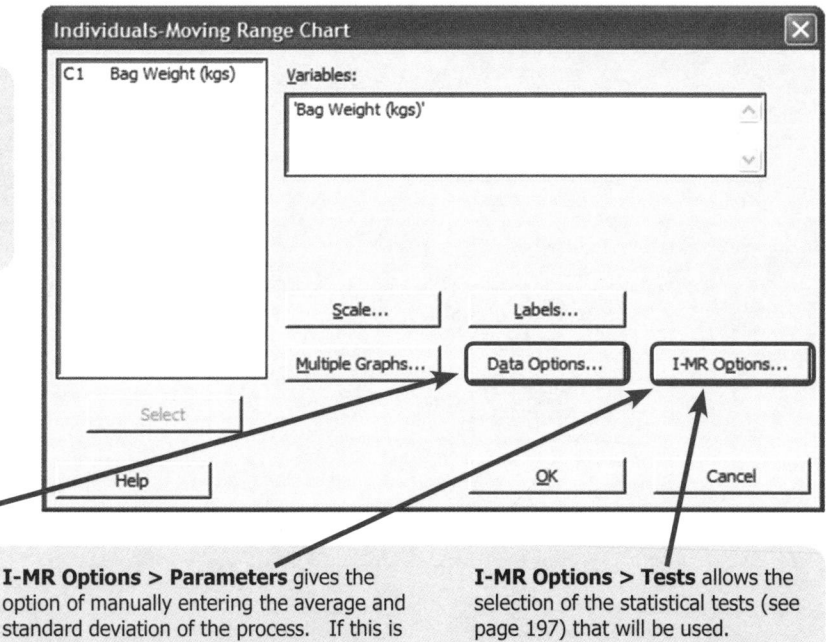

I-MR Options > Parameters gives the option of manually entering the average and standard deviation of the process. If this is done, then the I-MR will use these values to construct the control limits, instead of calculating them from the data. Page 203 gives an example that uses this option.

I-MR Options > Tests allows the selection of the statistical tests (see page 197) that will be used.

If in doubt, select **Perform all tests.**

I-MR Chart (Individual – Moving Range) – Output

I-MR Charts are actually a combination of two SPC charts, as shown here and described below.

The **Individuals (I) chart** (top) shows a Time Series plot of the data with control limits. The control limits are set at 3 Sigma (3 standard deviations) away from the average (middle line).

In this case, the process appears to be stable around about 31 kilos, and it doesn't go outside of the control limits. Accordingly, none of SPC tests (p197) have been broken.

The **Moving Range (MR) chart** (bottom) shows the moving range of the data in the top chart. So, for example, data point 3 on the lower chart is the range (the difference) between data points 2 & 3 on the top chart, and so on.

The range of a process is a reflection of the amount of variation in the process, and so the MR chart can be useful to detect changes in variation, but does not detect changes in average.

 "SPC-I-MR.mpj"

This high fluctuation is detected in the lower chart.

Point 15 fails test 1, since it is outside of the control limit.

Example: As explained on the page above, these charts represent the weight of sand in a sample of 50 bags at a building materials company.

The top chart indicates the process average is stable, because none of the tests were failed. However, data point 15 on the lower **Moving Range** chart has failed a test because it is outside of the control limits. This indicates a local increase in range (variation), which can actually be observed in the top chart – where there is a large fluctuation (circled).

So, although the **average** is stable, there is an indication that the **variation** is not.

X Bar-R Chart (Average – Range) – Input

X Bar-R Charts are used with small subgroups of Continuous data. Unlike I-MR charts, the raw data does **not** have to be Normally distributed for X Bar-R charts.

Example: A share trading company has completed a project that has reduced the average time it takes for its share/stock instructions to be traded, down to an average of 20.6 minutes.

They are now monitoring the process by randomly selecting 5 consecutive trades each day and plotting them on an SPC chart to check for process changes.

The X Bar-R chart is a suitable choice of chart because they have small subgroups of Continuous data being collected over a longer time period.

This particular example is using the SPC chart for 'ongoing control'(see page 198), and therefore the control limits on the chart need to be set around the new average of 20.6 minutes, as described here:

❗ **Subgroup size does not need to be constant.**
This example has a constant subgroup size of 5, but the XBar-R chart can deal with subgroup sizes that change.

  "SPC-XBar-R.mpj"

Minitab: Stat > Control Charts > Variable Charts for Subgroups > Xbar-R

Xbar-R Chart

| C1 | Time to trade |
| C2 | Sub-Group |

All observations for a chart are in one column:

'Time to trade'

If you have a constant subgroup size you can enter it here. Otherwise, enter the worksheet column that contains the subgroup number.

Subgroup sizes: 'Sub-Group' (enter a number or ID column)

Scale... | Labels...
Multiple Graphs... | Data Options... | Xbar-R Options...

Select

Help | OK | Cancel

Xbar-R Options > Parameters gives the option of manually entering the average and standard deviation of the process.
In this example the new average of 20.6 can be entered, in order to centre the control limits on the chart around this value.

Xbar-R Options > Tests allows the statistical tests (see page 197) that will be used for the analysis to be selected.
If in doubt, select **Perform all tests**

X Bar-R Chart (Average - Range) – Output

The average of subgroup number 8 is approximately 20.

The range of subgroup number 8 is very low (approx. 2).

X Bar - R Charts are actually a combination of two SPC charts, as shown here on the left and described below:

The **X Bar chart** (top) shows a Time Series plot of the averages of the subgroups with control limits.   The control limits are set based on the variation in the averages.

In this case, the average line is at 20.6 minutes, because this was defined at the data input stage (previous page). No tests have been failed, and so the process appears to be stable and does not appear to have moved from the new average trading time of 20.6 minutes.

The **Range (R) chart** (bottom) shows the range of the data that is within each subgroup.

Subgroup 8 is explained in detail on the chart as an example.

The range of a process is a reflection of its variation and so the R chart can be useful to detect changes in variation, but it does not detect changes in average.

 "SPC-XBar-R.mpj"

Example: As explained on the page above, these charts represent the time taken from instruction to completion of a trade on the stock exchange.

No tests have been failed on either chart, and so both the average and the variation of the process could be described as 'stable' or 'in-control'.

U Chart – Input

U Charts are for use with Count data, such as counting defects, or counting phone calls, or counting hospital operations.

Example: A human resource department is looking at the number of internal applications they receive for each vacancy that they advertise.

They have 15 weeks of historical data available for analysis (sample shown below) in order to understand if the number of internal applications per vacancy is stable (in-control) or changing over time.

C1	C2	C3
Week Number	Number of applications	Number of posts advertised
1	12	4
2	13	6
3	1	2
4	6	3
	6	5

! Subgroup size does not need to be constant.
The number of posts advertised each week is not constant, but the U-chart can accommodate this because it analyses the number of applications **per post/vacancy** advertised.

💾 **"SPC – U Chart.mpj"**

Minitab: Stat > Control Charts > Attributes Charts > U

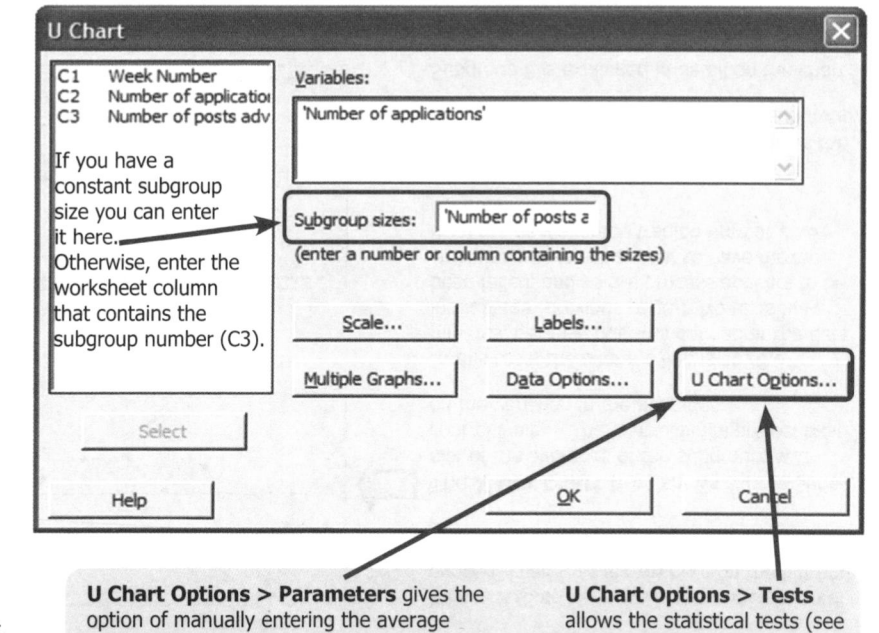

U Chart Options > Parameters gives the option of manually entering the average Defects per unit (DPU).
In this example, the SPC chart is being used to analyse historical data, so there is little reason to stipulate an average DPU.

U Chart Options > Tests allows the statistical tests (see page 197) that will be used for the analysis to be selected.
If in doubt, select **Perform all tests**

U Chart – Output

Week 6 has the widest control limits (and the smallest sample size).

Week 10 shows a higher than expected result, which is outside the control limits.

Week Number

Applications / Vacancy

The **U Chart** shows a Time Series plot of the average 'DPU' (Defects per Unit), for each subgroup. In this case, the 'DPU' is the number of internal applications per vacancy, and each subgroup represents a week.

Because the subgroup size (the number of vacancies posted each week) varies, the control limits adjust from week to week to reflect the different subgroup sizes.

For example, week 6 has the lowest sample size (only one vacancy was posted that week) and so the control limits expand to reflect this. This is because a much higher or lower result for week 6 is more likely given the low subgroup size.

The middle line is the overall average 'DPU' (in this case the average number of internal applications per vacancy advertised, over the 15 week period, is 2).

Example: As explained on the page above, this chart shows the average number of internal applications per vacancy advertised over a 20 week period.

The chart shows no clear rise or fall in the results, but week 10 shows an unexpectedly high result, which should be investigated further.

C-Charts work in a similar way to U charts, but they require the subgroup size to be constant.

If the number of job vacancies posted was a constant number each week, then a C-Chart **or** a U-Chart could have been used.

🖫 **"SPC – U Chart.mpj"**

P Chart – Input

P Charts are for use with Attribute data (usually summarised as proportions or percentages).

Example: A car breakdown service has noticed an increase in the proportion of vehicles that do not have 'functional' spare tyres over the summer months.

The team has 20 weeks of historical data from spring to autumn for analysis. Each week a random selection of drivers were asked if they had functional spare tyre in their car, and the result was recorded as shown below.

C1	C2
Number without spare tyre	**Number of drivers questioned**
7	59
5	47
7	48
6	67
10	

❗ Sub-group size does not need to be constant.

The number of drivers questioned each week is not constant, but the P-chart can accommodate this because it analyses the **proportion** of cars without a spare.

 "SPC – P Chart.mpj"

Minitab: Stat > Control Charts > Attributes Charts > P

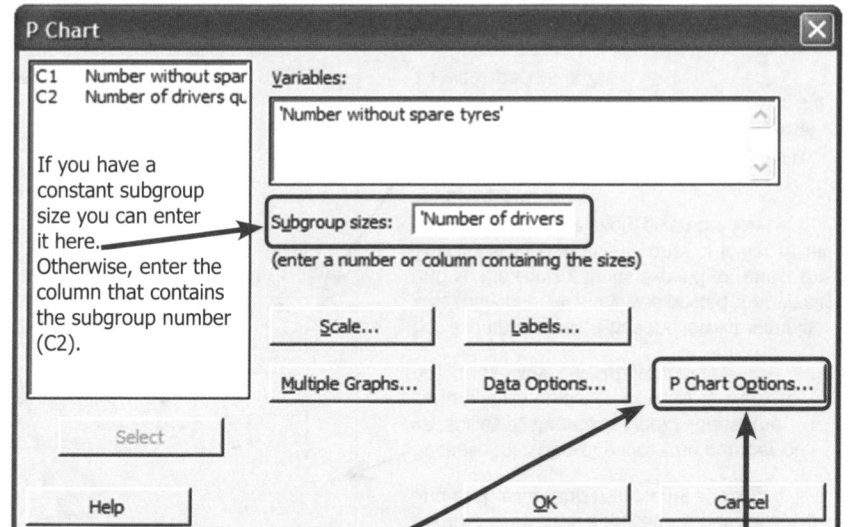

P Chart Options > Parameters gives the option of manually entering the overall proportion.

In this example, the SPC chart is being used to analyse historical data so there is little reason to enter an historical proportion value.

P Chart Options > Tests allows the statistical tests (see page 197) that will be used for the analysis to be selected.

If in doubt, select **Perform all tests**

P Chart – Output

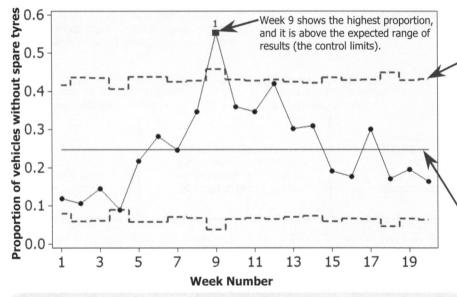

The **P Chart** shows a Time Series plot of the proportion for each subgroup (each week).

Because the subgroup/sample size (the number of drivers questioned) varies, the control limits adjust from week to week to reflect the different subgroup sizes.

For example, week 9 has the lowest sample size (only 38 drivers were questions that week) and so the control limits expand slightly to reflect this. This is because a much higher or lower result for week 9 is more likely, given the smaller subgroup.

(Taken to an extreme, if only one driver were questioned, the result could only be 0% or 100%!)

The middle line is the overall proportion of vehicles without functional spare tyres (over the entire 20 week period), which in this case is 0.247 (24.7%).

Example: As explained on the page above this chart shows the proportion of vehicles without functional spare tyres over a 20 week period. The chart shows a very clear rise and fall in the results which supports the team's original hypothesis – that there is an increase in the proportion of vehicles without spare tyres during the summer months. This is supported (statistically) by the fact that the data point for week 9 is outside of the control limits.

NP-Charts work in a similar way to P charts but they require the subgroup size to be constant.

If the number of drivers questioned each week had been the same, then an NP-Chart **or** a P-Chart could have been used.

"SPC – P Chart.mpj"

Control Plans

For each process step, a control plan defines the characteristics that are measured, their specification, historical capability, the measurement method used, and a response plan if out of specification.

Process: Each key process step is listed.

Specification: For each characteristic measured, the specification (or tolerance or target) are noted.

Measurement: The method of measurement and historical GR&R results are recorded (if available – see page 57). The data collection plan (sample size and frequency) and format for recording the measurement are also detailed.

Measures: Details of the input and output characteristics measured for each process step.

Capability: The historical capability is noted (if available) with the date of study.

Response: When an out of specification result is recorded, the response plan details how to ensure that no defects will reach the customer (containment) and how to 'fix' the process (adjustment).

What is a control plan? A control plan is a process management document that summarises the measurement details (what?, where?, when?, how? etc.) for each process step.

The components of a typical control plan are shown above, and can be seen to summarise many of the essential Six Sigma tools (process mapping, process measures, Voice of the Customer, process capability, GR&R, sampling, etc.)

FMEA and Control Plans: A control plan has similar elements to a Failure Mode and Effect Analysis (FMEA – page 100), but both documents have a distinct role to play as process management tools.

FMEAs are used to identify and assess risks, and to document existing controls in a process. Control plans provide increased detail on the measurement controls that will remain in place as 'business as usual' after a Six Sigma project is closed.

Standardised Processes

Successful solutions must become 'business as usual' in order to remain effective over the long term.

Standardised Processes is the phrase given to ensuring solutions have been embedded into the organisation's methods and procedures. A "standardised process" provides more consistent results since the variation is reduced by ensuring a task is always done the same way.

How to standardise your projects solutions:

1) **Understand the organisation's existing systems for standardising processes.** These may by written instructions, visual examples, training programs, drawings, revision controls etc.

2) **Challenge the existing systems before using them.** There is no point standardising a process into systems and procedures that do not currently work. Identify the methods and procedures that are successful in your organisation and use them.

3) **Document your project solutions.** Ensure the new process and procedures are clearly explained, with no ambiguity.

Whilst developing your standardised processes, do not forget to...
- Be innovative! – develop new systems if necessary.
- Ensure clear ownership.
- Use visual / practical systems wherever possible.
- Ensure any legal or auditing obligations are met.

Project Report & Action Log

Successful projects have a clear, timely and controlled closure. Knowing when to close a project is a balance between making sure all the actions are completed and maintaining a focus on the pace of a project.

Successful Six Sigma programs have clear visibility on the status of projects (open or closed) and a strong emphasis on transferring the lessons learnt from projects to provide gains elsewhere in the organisation. This is sometimes referred to as 'leveraging'.

Components of a Project Report

- Clear storyboard through the DMAIC phases of the project, with summaries of the key conclusions, decisions and solutions.
- Keywords (for successful archiving / knowledge management).
- Lessons Learnt (for transfer).
- Clear records and access to data used (incl. Minitab files etc.) .
- Closure Action Log (see below).

Closure Action Log

All outstanding actions should be documented at project closure with clear responsibility and target dates for completion.

A review of the action log should be planned for 3-6 months.

Ownership of the process in the short term should be clear, with identified handovers.

Control – Checklist

❏ Have ongoing KPIs been developed to monitor performance?

❏ Have they been integrated into the organisations KPI structure (dashboards/scorecards etc.) where possible/necessary?

❏ Have data collection plans for the ongoing KPIs been implemented as "business as usual"?

❏ Do the KPIs and data collection plans have clear owners?

❏ Have relevant graphical and statistical techniques been implemented to help the new owners monitor and review process performance?　(SPC, histograms, run charts etc.)

❏ Have the improvements been documented, 'standardised' and become "business as usual"?

❏ Have the improvements in the KPIs been quantified, and new baselines established?

❏ Have the project savings been calculated and signed off with finance department agreement?

❏ Has the project report been completed, and lessons learnt communicated to other relevant areas?

Control – Review Questions

▪ How were the ongoing KPIs selected?

▪ Have the temporary data collection plans for the project been removed?

▪ Who owns the KPIs now?　Who will be monitoring them?

▪ Have the new KPI owners been helped to understand **how** to monitor the KPIs?

▪ How will we know if the process performance deteriorates?　What alarm bells will ring?

▪ What has been done to ensure the improvements have become business as usual and won't 'fall over' after the project closes?

▪ By how much did the problem (and COPQ) reduce?

▪ What are the validated project savings?

▪ Where did the savings eventually come from? (efficiency, cash flow - cost of capital, scrap, reduced costs etc.)

▪ What next?　Is there anywhere else in the organisation that the project learnings can be used?

APPENDICES

Recommended Six Sigma Partners

There is a large range of Six Sigma products and service providers on the market, so it can be a time consuming process selecting the right one. As a leading training and coaching company, QSB Consulting can recommend the following providers within their field of expertise:

For **Six Sigma Conferences** that help you keep up to date with advances in Six Sigma, try **IQPC's Six Sigma conferences** (p214)

For **Project Companion software** that guides you through your projects, try **Quality Companion 2 from Minitab** (p215)

For **Simulation Modelling software** that helps you simulate, optimise and forecast your processes, try **Crystal Ball** (p217)

For **Programme Management software** that helps you manage your continuous improvement initiatives, try **i-nexus** (p219)

For a **Six Sigma web portal** that provides online access to Six Sigma information, try **www.onesixsigma.com** (p221)

For **Lean Six Sigma training and project coaching** contact us at QSB Consulting; **www.QSBC.co.uk**

For the **interactive Six Sigma guide** that accompanies this book, try the **Six Sigma Tool Finder** (see inside back cover)

The Six Sigma IQ Mission

Six Sigma IQ (a Division of IQPC) is the world's leading provider of Six Sigma, Lean and Process Improvement summits. It is our mission to stimulate thought-provoking dialogue and lively exchange between principal quality specialists through our forums, workshops, structured networking sessions, annual Six Sigma Excellence Awards and e-updates.

Who speaks at Six Sigma IQ Summits?

There is no better place to experience this than at our **Summits**, with first class speaker line ups including **Jack Welch**, **General Colin Powell, USA (Ret.), and Rudy Giuliani**, Former **Mayor of New York City** - you can't afford to miss out!

What will you get out of a six sigma IQ Summit?

Hear from big industry names and network with over 300 of your senior Quality and Six Sigma peers including:

CEOs, CQOs, COOs	Directors of Six Sigma
VPs of Quality and Productivity	Master Black Belts
VPs of Business Excellence	Black Belts Directors of Quality
VPs of Continuous Improvement	

Upcoming six sigma IQ Summits

8th Annual Six Sigma Summit Miami 2007

January 2007 ·   Miami, USA

8th Annual Six Sigma Summit London 2007

April 2007 · London, UK

European Lean Six Sigma Summit 2007

October 2007 · Amsterdam, The Netherlands

For more details, visit our website at:

www.sixsigmasummit.com

Quality Companion 2 ▷ ™
by Minitab

Process improvement software made for Six Sigma

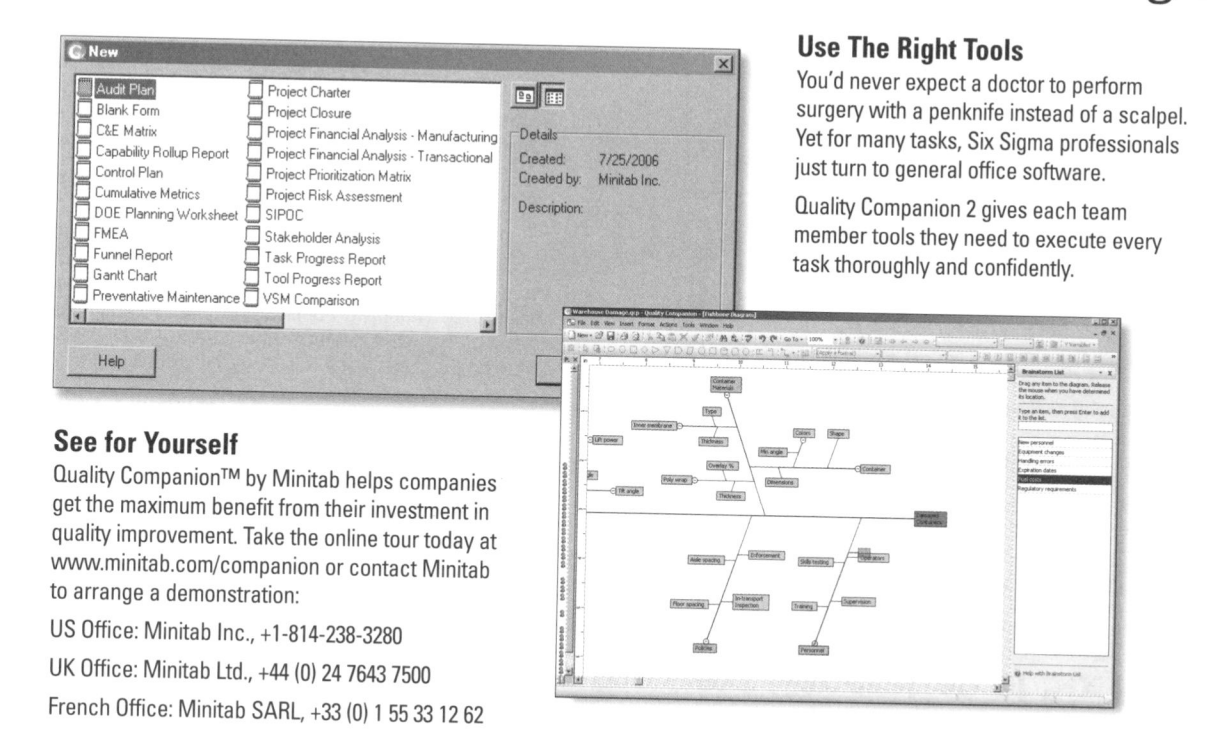

Use The Right Tools

You'd never expect a doctor to perform surgery with a penknife instead of a scalpel. Yet for many tasks, Six Sigma professionals just turn to general office software.

Quality Companion 2 gives each team member tools they need to execute every task thoroughly and confidently.

See for Yourself

Quality Companion™ by Minitab helps companies get the maximum benefit from their investment in quality improvement. Take the online tour today at www.minitab.com/companion or contact Minitab to arrange a demonstration:

US Office: Minitab Inc., +1-814-238-3280

UK Office: Minitab Ltd., +44 (0) 24 7643 7500

French Office: Minitab SARL, +33 (0) 1 55 33 12 62

> Done properly, Six Sigma streamlines processes, reduces errors, and increases profits. But Six Sigma is hard, and doing it *right* is even harder. *Unless you have the right tools.*

Quality Companion 2 by Minitab helps companies take command of their projects. This tool makes it easy to do Six Sigma right by providing three key elements in a single package:

- ▶ Organizational power
- ▶ Practical "soft" tools for project tasks
- ▶ Expert guidance on demand

Organizational Power

Quality Companion's Project Roadmap™ organizes projects into phases and creates a launch pad for the tools each requires. Master Black Belts can easily create custom roadmaps to guide teams through any project.

Quality Companion maintains all project documents, even ones created outside the program, in one file. Teams have instant access to the entire project with a single click.

Quality Companion also shares data, so teams needn't worry about updating forms and tools. Data entered or updated in one tool, like the process map, automatically populate other tools, like the C&E matrix.

Practical Six Sigma Tools

Quality Companion provides integrated "soft" tools for tasks like brainstorming, process mapping, assessing risk, and conducting analyses such as SIPOC and FMEA. Teams can even deliver presentations without leaving the software.

It features more than 100 ready-to-use forms, including project charter and closure forms, control plans, funnel reports, DOE worksheets, and more. And every tool and form is fully customizable.

Guidance

Quality Companion's Coach feature helps guide teams through projects. It informs teams which analyses are appropriate for every phase, and why. It explains how to use each tool correctly and avoid common errors.

Master Black Belts can add information to the Coach to help their teams. Companies can even create new coaches with their own guidelines and materials.

Green and Black Belts

Without a clear framework to follow, new Six Sigma practitioners often struggle with knowing what steps to take when. Quality Companion's Project Roadmap points them in the right direction while the Coach provides expert guidance as needed. Combined with Quality Companion's entire collection of tools, belts can get through projects with confidence.

Master Black Belts

Master Black Belts can anticipate their teams' concerns and include answers right in Quality Companion. That makes deployments smooth and efficient and lets leaders devote more time to higher-level mentoring and projects.

Champions

Quality Companion automatically documents a team's progress in detail, so that Champions can see as much about a project as they wish at any time.

Crystal Ball *Simulation Modeling Software*

What is Crystal Ball?

Crystal Ball, a Microsoft® Excel® based suite of software tools, provides Monte Carlo simulation, optimisation, and forecasting techniques that can help you predict capability, pinpoint critical-to-quality factors, and explore design alternatives.

How Does Crystal Ball Complement Minitab?

Minitab's strengths include analysing data, planning experiments, and visualising the data. Crystal Ball takes this analysis a step further by letting you simulate and optimise system performance. A system is a mathematical model such as an electronic circuit, a mechanical component, or even a transactional process.

What Types of Problems Does Crystal Ball Solve?

Crystal Ball is especially useful when data is infrequent, unavailable, or costly to acquire, because simulation can create a sample of output (response) data based on input distributions (see the case study on the next page). Common applications include cost estimation, tolerance analysis, design optimisation, process improvement, and reliability studies.

Where Does Crystal Ball Fit Into The DMAIC Process?

DEFINE: Project and financial managers use simulation to account for cost, schedule, and success uncertainty and to test the impacts of a proposed change on customer satisfaction and profitability.

MEASURE: Simulation can provide a baseline process and capability measurement and can be used to estimate infrequent, costly, or nonexistent data.

ANALYSE: Sensitivity analysis helps to uncover and validate the underlying causes of variation and waste; it works equally well as a communication tool for building consensus and gaining early approval of process owners.

IMPROVE: Simulation and stochastic optimisation can help save on expenses, resources, and time by allowing you to experiment on proposed process changes prior to implementation.

Try Crystal Ball today!

Visit the Crystal Ball Web site today and download a trial version: http://www.crystalball.com/qsbc

Crystal Ball *Simulation Modeling Software*

Crystal Ball and Minitab Case Study:
DoE with Simulation

A Six Sigma team attempted to improve a process that involved manufacturing plastic-injected molded parts. These parts had to meet length specifications, but variation in the process resulted in incomplete filling of the mold and different part lengths.

In the project Measure phase, the team collected measurements of mold temperature, cycle time, and hold pressure for 150 parts. In Minitab, each of these datasets passed a normality test. The team used these three factors as the basis for a Design of Experiments.

The team defined, conducted, and analysed an experiment with eight runs in a full factorial 2^3 treatment structure. The DoE included five replicates of the eight runs for a total of 40 trials. All of the main effects - mold temperature, cycle time, and hold pressure - had significant impact on part length, as did the interaction between mold temperature and cycle time. From the reduced model, Minitab created a nonlinear transfer function for the part length.

The team then moved the function to Microsoft Excel to learn more about how the part length responded to variations in the three control factors. The team first used Crystal Ball software to define each of the three factors as a normal distribution with mean and standard deviation taken from the measure data.

They then used Crystal Ball to test the capability of the transfer function by running a Monte Carlo simulation of 1000 trials, the equivalent of creating 1,000 virtual plastic parts! The output histogram is shown on the right.

The simulation results showed that the part length process passed the normality test with a P-value of 0.752, that the defect rate was 2.35%, and that the sigma level was 1.95. The process was off center to the right, with a C_{PK} of 0.65. This indicated that more parts were longer than average instead of shorter than average.

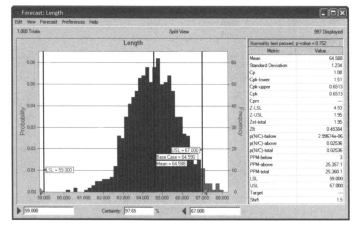

Sensitivity analysis from the simulation revealed that part length variation was greatly influenced (~50%) by the variation in the mold temperature. The team found that they could halve the mold temperature standard deviation, and they ran a subsequent simulation using this new parameter, resulting in a sigma level of 2.5 with less than 1% defects. The team continued on with a stochastic optimisation that used Crystal Ball to minimise the process cost while maximising the process Sigma Level.

Program Management Software

Our message is very simple....

i-nexus is the leading enterprise software for managing a lean six sigma program.

With our software, our customers see an average 25% increase on their return on investment in Lean Six Sigma.

Our customers get these results not just because **i-nexus** has the features needed to pick better projects, save time, engage sponsors and leverage successes across the organization but because it is easy – easy to use, easy to deploy and easy to evolve.

From use as a simple belt support tool during the lean six sigma training process through to use a tool to drive strategic alignment throughout the whole organization, **i-nexus** starts simple and grows with your needs.

For The Belt:

- **Saves you time**
  - Simple project reporting/storyboards
  - Quick access to tools/templates
  - Leverage existing corporate knowledge

- **Keeps your sponsor engaged**
  - Real-time alerts
  - Sends reports to their inbox

- **Keeps your team engaged**
  - Collaborate on deliverables
  - Allocate and track task completion

For The Deployment Leader:

- **Drives greater return on your investment**
  - Systematic project selection
  - Provides $Y=f(x)$ insights on ROI drivers
  - Provides in-depth portfolio analysis

- **Keeps your senior management engaged**
  - Personalised reporting with clear line of sight from business goals to improvement projects
  - Full drill-down capabilities

- **Makes it easy for you to administrate program**
  - Simple training and certification management
  - Flexible/powerful financial reporting

For The Senior Manager:

- **Aligns your organisation behind strategic objectives**
  - Enables you to see if improvement efforts are producing results

- **Makes your organisation more agile and more profitable.**

For further information, contact:
i-nexus Europe   Tel: +44 845 607 0063
i-nexus America   Tel: +1   617 273 8387
i-nexus Asia   Tel: +86 215 108 7994
Email: sales@i-nexus.com web: www.i-nexus.com

onesixsigma.com

σnesixsigma.com
The voice of the Six Sigma professional in Europe

Services Directory

- Six Sigma & Lean Training Providers
- Six Sigma & Lean Consultants
- Six Sigma & Lean Software
- Quality Institutes
- Business Schools & Research Centres

Knowledge Centre

- Comprehensive Glossary
- Tools & Techniques
- Subject Matters
- Methods & Models
- Articles & White Papers
- Project Storyboards
- Recommended Publications

Community

- User Group Meetings
- Leadership Breakfasts
- Discussion Forums
- Feature Interviews
- Events Calendar

Professional Development

- Six Sigma & Lean Jobs
- Technical Exams
- Awareness Tests
- Salary Surveys
- Public Training

onesixsigma.com

Who We Are

onesixsigma.com was established as the only **independent** dedicated **European Six Sigma online information portal** in 2003. Since then, using a customer-centric, diligent and innovative approach, we have grown to become the hub for **Service Providers** and **Benchmarking User Communities**. Focused on Europe, we remain autonomous, unbiased and are truly practitioner led.

What We do

Working in partnership with the leading Six Sigma and Lean service providers in Europe, we offer unparalleled access to **industry information** in one fully interactive place. These **comprehensive** resources, as outlined above, are fully **searchable** and **easy to navigate** with **real-life applications** and interactive examples and templates.

We **bring together** like-minded business leaders, Six Sigma and Lean professionals of all levels to **exchange ideas**, **benchmark performance**, and **build frameworks** for improving business transformation; through both our online and offline services we provide a **safe forum** for understanding the huge diversity in the **applications of methods and tools** for process specialists, change agents, deployment leaders, executives & champions, consultants & training providers, and statisticians & academia.

How We Do It

In order to remain at the core of the industry, we **build partnerships** with leading Six Sigma and Lean **Consultants, Training Providers, Software Vendors, Research Centres, Quality Institutes**, and **Thought Leaders**. Our **online platform** is **constantly evolving** to the needs of our clients and users, and to ensure it is the main outlet for new industry developments and upcoming events, job opportunities and experiences documented in the form of articles and feature interviews. Further, we organise, administrate, market and manage **offline User Group Meetings**; bringing together an **unbiased collective** of **cross-industry** business improvement specialists to communicate ideas and experiences, and provide a valuable **knowledge-sharing** and **networking** service.

What You Can Do

Visit www.onesixsigma.com. Sign up for our regular monthly newsletter to be informed of latest Six Sigma and Lean community developments. Whether you are a newcomer to Six Sigma or an experienced professional and have bought this book as a practical reference and resource tool, contact us to **join the practitioner community** and your local User Group. If you are a Six Sigma and Lean Service Provider, contact us about our **Partner Programmes** to ensure your brand is at the forefront of the industry and to take advantage of the outstanding promotional opportunities available.

For more information, contact the onesixsigma.com team on **0870 145 1616** or email **info@onesixsigma.com**

Quick Guide to 'p-values' (based on 95% Confidence)

The Tool	P-Value < 0.05	P-Value > 0.05
Anderson Darling Normality Test	You can be confident that your data **is not** Normally distributed.	You can assume that your data **is** Normally distributed.
1 Sample t-Test (against a known value)	You can be confident that your sample has a **different** average from the known test value.	There is **no difference** between your sample average and the known test value (based on the data you have).
2 Sample t-Test	You can be confident that the averages of the two samples are **different**.	There is **no difference** between the averages of the two samples (based on the data you have).
Paired t-Test	You can be confident that there is a consistent **difference** between the pairs of data.	There is **no consistent difference** between the pairs of data (based on the data you have).
One Way ANOVA	You can be confident that at least one of the samples has a **different** average from the others.	There is **no difference** in the averages of the samples (based on the data you have).
Kruskal Wallis & Mood's Median Test	You can be confident that at least one of the samples has a **different** median from the others.	There is **no difference** in the medians of the samples (based on the data you have).

Distribution Identification

Hypothesis Testing Continuous Data

Quick Guide to p-values (based on 95% Confidence)

The Tool	P-Value < 0.05	P-Value > 0.05
F-test, Levene's test Bartlett's test	You can be confident that at least one of your samples has a **different** standard deviation from the others.	There is **no difference** between the standard deviations of the samples (based on the data you have).
1 Proportion (against a known value)	You can be confident that your sample has a **different** proportion from the known test value.	There is **no difference** between your sample proportion and the known test value (based on the data you have).
2 Proportion	You can be confident that the proportions from the two samples are **different**.	There is **no difference** between the proportions from the two samples (based on the data you have).
Chi-Square	You can be confident that at least one of the samples has a **different** proportion from the others.	There is **no difference** in the proportions from the samples (based on the data you have).
Correlation (Pearson Coefficient)	You can be confident that there **is** a correlation (Pearson coefficient is not zero).	There is **no correlation** (based on the data you have). (Pearson coefficient could be zero)
Regression	You can be confident that the input factor (predictor) affects the process output.	There is **no correlation** between the input factor (predictor) and the process output (based on the data you have).

Hypothesis Testing Attribute Data (rows: 1 Proportion, 2 Proportion, Chi-Square)

Correlation and Regression (rows: Correlation, Regression)

QSB Consulting – Six Sigma Minitab Menu (Versions 14, 15)

A major improvement of Minitab versions 14 and 15 is the introduction of customisable menus which allow you to group together your favourite tools into one menu.

The **QSB Consulting Six Sigma Menu** is a (free) ready made menu that brings together all of the tools described in this guide. The structure of the QSB menu is shown on the next page.

The menu is contained within a file which can be downloaded online. The file should be imported as a profile file into Minitab (14 or 15) as described below.   In doing so, note that:

▪ All of the standard menus will be unaffected.
▪ The new menu can be easily switched off if you do not require it anymore, by removing the profile from the active list.

Installing the QSB Six Sigma Menu:

▪ Download the profile file (opposite) and save to your local disk.
▪ In Minitab, open the **Manage Profiles** function (opposite).
▪ Click **Import** and navigate to the file. Click **Open**.
▪ The 'QSBC – Customised Minitab Menu' profile should now be shown in the **Available profile** list.
▪ Transfer it to the **Active profile** list.
▪ Ensure the QSBC profile is at the **top** of the **Active profiles** list by using the arrows indicated. Click **OK**.

Minitab: Tools > Manage Profiles

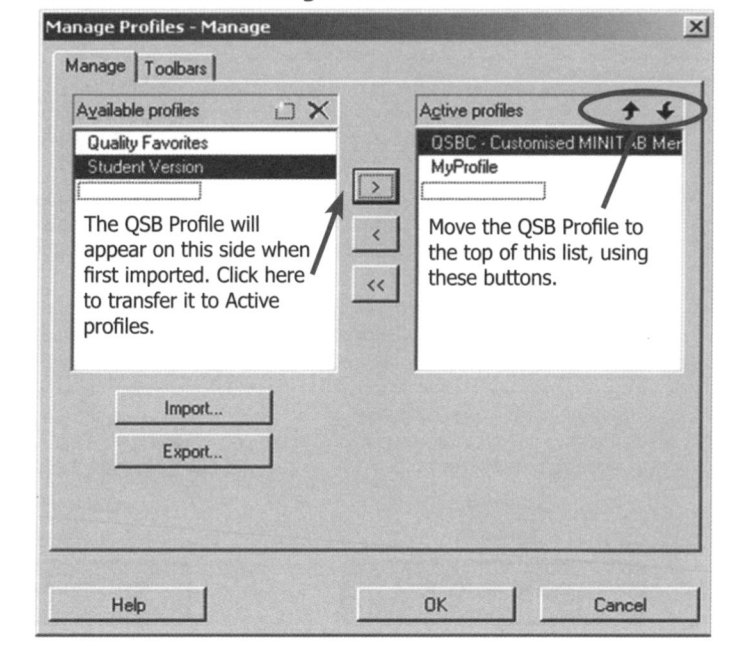

The QSB Profile will appear on this side when first imported. Click here to transfer it to Active profiles.

Move the QSB Profile to the top of this list, using these buttons.

"QSBC Customised Minitab Menu.reg"

Free download available online at www.QSBC.co.uk

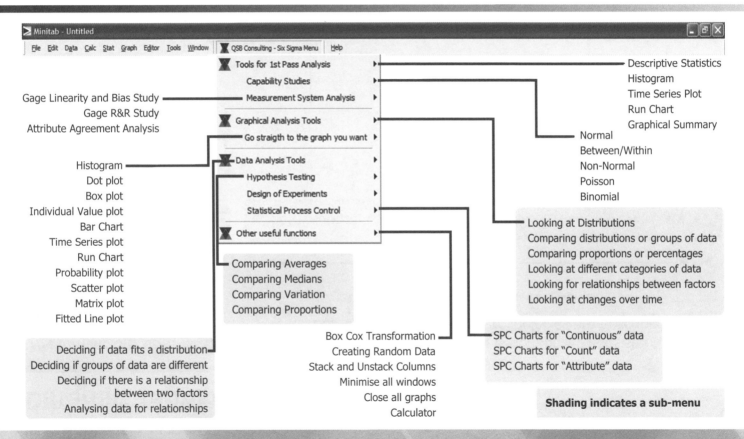

Different Terminology for Data Worlds

The terminology used for the different data worlds within Six Sigma is not applied consistently across consultancies, training providers or texts. Some of the alternative terminologies are described here.

Sometimes the Count and Attribute data worlds are grouped together (as Discrete or Attribute data). However this ignores the fundamental differences between these two data worlds, and the statistical models on which they are based.

Central Limit Theorem

What is the Central Limit Theorem?

The Central Limit Theorem (CLT) is a useful statistical theory that applies behind the scenes of several Six Sigma tools and techniques.

The theorem says that if you take lots of subgroups of data from a population and plot their averages, the averages will always be (approximately) Normally distributed, regardless of the shape of the population distribution.

So, even if the population is skewed to the left or the right, the subgroup averages will be Normally distributed as shown here on the right:

Where is the Central Limit Theorem (CLT) used?

The Central Limit Theorem is not used as a tool in its own right but it is at work behind the scenes of some of the Six Sigma tools in this text. For example:

- When calculating **Confidence Intervals** for an average, the CLT means that the interval is symmetrical.
- In **Statistical Process Control** the CLT means that the XBar-R chart (which plots averages of subgroups) can be used with non-Normal data.

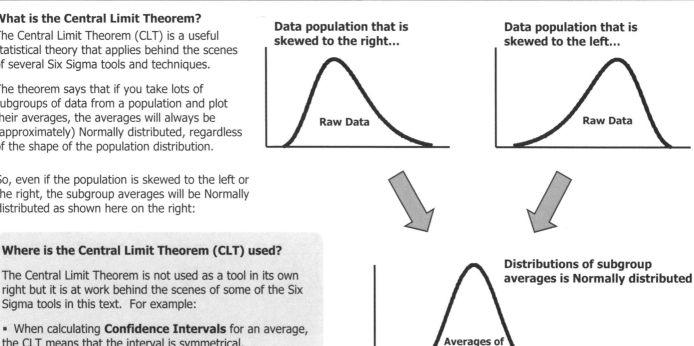

Data population that is skewed to the right...

Raw Data

Data population that is skewed to the left...

Raw Data

Distributions of subgroup averages is Normally distributed

Averages of subgroups

Analysis of Variance (ANOVA)

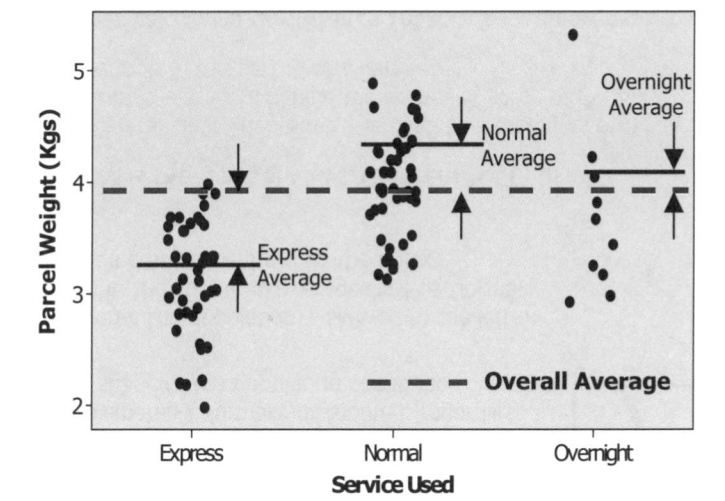

What is Analysis of Variance (ANOVA)?

ANOVA is a mathematical technique that separates out the different sources of variation within a sample of data.

Using the example from pages 93 & 95, the parcel weights for different types of courier service are shown on the left.

ANOVA can be used to find out how much of the total variation in parcel weight is attributable to the different service types, and how much is left over ('residual' variation).

How does ANOVA work?

ANOVA works on the following principle:

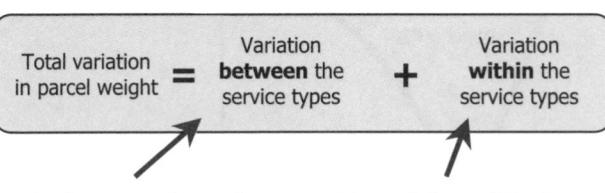

The variation **between** the service types is calculated by studying the variation of the subgroup averages around the Overall Average (as indicated on the Individual Value plot).

The variation **within** the service types is calculated by studying each subgroup separately.

Where is ANOVA used?   ANOVA is at work behind the scenes in many of the tools and techniques of Six Sigma.

- In **GR&R** it is used to identify the relative variation caused by the gauge and the appraiser.
- In **Regression** it is used to identify the relative variation caused by the different process inputs.
- In **DOE** it is used to assess the relative variation caused by input factors and their interactions.

"Courier-Process.mpj"

Box Cox Transformation

What is the Box Cox Transformation?

If your data is **not** Normally distributed it can restrict the use of certain tools and techniques. The Box Cox Transformation is a method of mathematically converting the data so that it becomes Normally distributed (for the purpose of analysis only). Decisions and analysis can then be completed on the transformed data.

The Box Cox Transformation in Minitab:

As shown below, the Box Cox transformation uses a constant called 'lambda'. Minitab can be set to find the 'Optimal Lambda' that is most likely to produce a Normal distribution in the transformed data.

Minitab: Stat > Control Charts > Box Cox Transformation

Real data

This real data (below) is quite clearly **not** Normally distributed. This means that the Z-table cannot be used to predict the percentage of defects that are above the spec limit.

Upper Specification Limit (USL)

Skewed Distribution

Defects

Mathematical Transformation

Each unit of raw data is 'transformed' to the power of Lambda:

$$X^\lambda$$

Transformed data

The Box Cox transformation creates a Normal distribution from the data. The Z-table can now be used to predict the area above the specification limit.

❗The specification limit must go through the transformation as well!

USL - Transformed

Normal Distribution

Defects

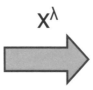

Why Normality?

The Normal distribution is a common concept throughout Six Sigma and so it is important for the Normal distribution to be understood in order that many of the tools and techniques can be applied in a statistically valid manner.

However, there is a danger that a Six Sigma trainee can leave training with the impression that a process that is not Normally distributed is not a good process!

Whilst it may limit the tools and techniques that can be used, this quite clearly is **not** the case.

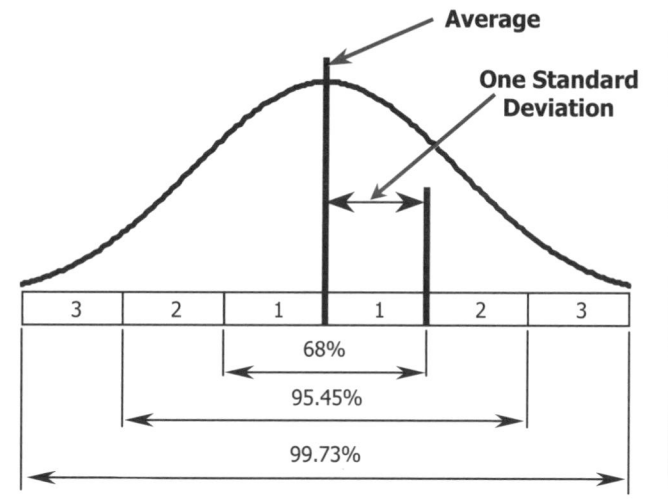

Where and how the Normal distribution is important...

For Capability Analysis: If we know the Normal distribution is behind a sample of data, then we can make predictions about the process capability over the longer term, using tools such as the Z-table.

For Confidence Intervals: The mathematics behind the calculation of a Confidence Interval for the average of a sample is based on the Normal distribution.

For Hypothesis Testing: Many hypothesis tests are based on the assumption that the data is Normally distributed. If this assumption is not correct then the results of these hypothesis test may be invalid.

For Correlation and Regression: The validity of a regression model can be assessed by analysing its 'residual errors'. If they are Normally distributed it indicates the regression model fits the data well.

For Statistical Process Control: Certain SPC charts require the data to be Normally distributed in order to be valid.

For Design of Experiments (DOE): Important input factors are identified during DOE analyses, by assessing those input factor effects that do not conform to the Normal distribution.

Six Sigma Acronyms

ANOVA	Analysis of Variance		IVP	Individual Value Plot
BB	Black Belt		JIT	Just In Time (scheduling)
BNVA	Business Non Value Add		KPI	Key Performance Indicator
BPR	Business Process Re-engineering		LCL	Lower Control Limit
CAP	Change Acceleration Process		LSL	Lower Specification Limit
CI	Confidence Interval		MBB	Master Black Belt
CLT	Central Limit Theorem		MSA	Measurement System Analysis
COPQ	Cost of Poor Quality		NVA	Non Value Add
CTQ	Critical To Quality		OFD	Opportunities for Defects
DFSS	Design for Six Sigma		PCE	Process Cycle Efficiency
DMADV	Define Measure, Analyse, Design, Verify		p(d)	Probability of a Defect
DMAIC	Define, Measure, Analyse, Improve, Control		PPM	Parts Per Million
DOE	Design Of Experiments		SD	Standard Deviation
DPMO	Defects per Million Opportunities		SIPOC	Suppliers, Inputs, Process, Outputs, Customers
DPU	Defects per Unit		SPC	Statistical Process Control
FMEA	Failure Mode and Effect Analysis		UCL	Upper Control Limit
FTY	First Time Yield		USL	Upper Specification Limit
GB	Green Belt		VA	Value Add
GDPM	Goal Directed Project Management		VOC	Voice of the Customer
GR&R	Gauge Repeatability and Reproducibility		VOP	Voice of the Process
Ha	Alternative Hypothesis		VSM	Value Stream Mapping
Ho	Null Hypothesis		WIP	Work In Progress
IDI	Individual Distribution Identification			

Six Sigma Glossary (excluding tools detailed in this guide)

Accuracy: A type of measurement system error, also referred to as Bias.

Alpha Risk: The risk of (mistakenly) deciding there is a difference in a hypothesis test, when there isn't.

Alternative Hypothesis (Ha):   An alternative hypothesis is used during hypothesis testing, and usually starts with "there is a difference between".   (Opposite to the Null Hypothesis).

Attribute Data: A type of data world that contains only 2 different categories of results (e.g. Good/Bad, Pass/Fail, On time / Not on time.)

Average: The arithmetic average aims to represent the middle position of a sample of data. It is calculated by adding all the results and dividing by the sample size.

Baseline: A value that represents the existing performance of a process, typically before an improvement project starts.

Bias: A type of measurement system error, Bias refers to any consistent differences between the true value and the measured value.

Binomial Distribution: The statistical distribution behind the attribute data world. The results of a dice or a pack of cards conform to the Binomial distribution.

Black Belt (BB):   A (usually full-time) Six Sigma practitioner who has completed 3-4 weeks of training and delivered several successful Six Sigma projects.

Business Non Value Add (BNVA):   A process step that adds no value to the product or service but is required for business purposes.

Business Process Re-engineering (BPR):   The process of analysing and re-building business processes in order to reduce complexity, remove non-value add work and deliver more customer focussed products and services.

Categorical Data: Non-numeric data that has distinct categories, such as different root causes or failure types etc.

Central Limit Theorem: A statistical theorem that states that the distribution of subgroup averages will be approximately Normal.

Champion: A sponsor of Six Sigma, responsible for gaining buy-in and facilitating a successful Six Sigma program at a senior level.

Common Cause Variation: Random variation that is predictable within a specific range, and indicates a stable process.

Confidence Interval (CI):   Based on a sample statistic, a CI is a range within which you can be confident (to a specified confidence level – usually 95%) that the real population statistic is within.

Contextual Data: Non-numeric information about where and when a piece of data came from. (e.g, serial numbers, dates, machine numbers, location, customer etc.)

Continuous Data: A type of data world that contains numeric data which has been 'measured', (such as temperature, time and distance etc.).

Cost of Poor Quality (COPQ):   The negative financial effects of a defect occurring are termed the Cost of Poor Quality.

Count Data: A numeric data world that contains results from 'counting' things. The Count data world only contains whole numbers (integers).

Critical to Quality (CTQ):   The features of a product or service that are critical to its quality from the voice of the customers perspective.

Data Door: A phrase given to a selection of graphical and statistical techniques used in the Analyse phase that focus on gaining clues from the data available.

Six Sigma Glossary (excluding tools detailed in this guide)

Data Worlds: Different types of data, each with distinctive qualities that determine the type of analysis and tools that should be used, (see the continuous, count and attribute data worlds).

Defect: A feature of a product or service that does not meet the customers requirements.

Design for Six Sigma (DFSS): The use of Six Sigma tools and techniques in the design of products, services and processes is called Design for Six Sigma. DFSS follows the DMADV flow.

Design of Experiments (DOE): A wide range of controlled experiments that are used to understand the relationship between the inputs and outputs of a process.

Discrete Data: The Count and Attribute data worlds are both 'discrete', because they can only be whole numbers (integers).

Entitlement: The difference between the process capability in the short and long term is referred to as the entitlement of the process, since a large difference indicates the process could be improved.

Goal Directed Project Management: A structured team based approach to planning and controlling projects.

Green Belt (GB): A (usually part-time) Six Sigma team member who has completed around 5 days of training and participated in several successful Six Sigma projects.

Hypothesis Testing: A structured approach that quantifies statistical confidence when making decisions based on data. A range of different hypothesis tests are available, depending on the situation and type of data.

In-Control: A process that is stable and under the influence of common cause variation only.

Jitter: The sideways scattering of data points on an Individual Value plot in order to prevent them overlapping (graphically).

Long Term: A time period during which all the inputs to the process have a chance to vary and affect the process.

Master Black Belt (MBB): A (full-time) Six Sigma practitioner who has completed Black Belt training and additional coaching/facilitation training. Typically also delivers training and coaches Black Belts.

Mean: An alternative word for Average

Measurement System Analysis (MSA): The process of challenging the quality of data through analysis of the measurement system, using tools such as Gauge R&R.

Median: The middle value of a sample of data; 50% of the data points fall above the median and 50% below. (The same as the 50% percentile).

Milestone: A key event within a project plan, a milestone has clear deliverables and is usually marked with a tollgate review.

Non Value Add (NVA): A process step that adds no value to the product or service (e.g. inspection).

Normal Distribution: A commonly occurring distribution that is symmetrical and 'bell-shaped'.

Outlier: A data point that is outside of the expected range of results, and is therefore likely to have been caused by special cause variation.

Out-of-Control: A process that is un-stable and under the influence of both common and special cause variation.

Poisson Distribution: The statistical distribution behind the Count data world.

Population: A statistical term that represents the entire population from which a data set was sampled.

Six Sigma Glossary (excluding tools detailed in this guide)

Precision: A type of measurement system error; precision refers to the level of variation/errors (in the data) that is caused by the measurement system itself.

Poisson Distribution: The statistical distribution behind the Count data world.

Population: A statistical term that represents the entire population from which a data set was sampled.

Precision: A type of measurement system error; precision refers to the level of variation/errors (in the data) that is caused by the measurement system itself.

Process Capability: The capability of the process to fulfil the customers requirements.

Process Door: A phrase given to the selection of tools used in the Analyse phase that focus on gaining clues from the process itself (process mapping etc.)

Process Stability: The extent to which a process has a predictable range of output or results over time.

Range: The difference between the highest and lowest values.

Resolution: The smallest difference that a measurement system is able to record (or discriminate).

Root Cause: The fundamental reason why a defect occurred.

Sample: A collection of data taken from a process.

Sample Size: The number of data points in a sample.

Short Term: A short time period during which only a few process inputs have a chance to vary and affect the process.

Sigma Level: The Six Sigma measure of process capability.

Sigma Shift: The difference between the short and long term Sigma Levels.

Special Cause Variation: Variation that is not predictable and usually caused by specific events. This type of variation creates an unstable process.

Specification: The limits of acceptability, as defined by the voice of the customer.

Standard Deviation: A measure of variation. Standard deviation represents the average variation of a sample of data points from their own average.

Stratification: The division of data into different subgroups based on categorical data (such as different locations or different products).

Subgroup: Often used interchangeably with "sample", a subgroup should be used to refer to a small sample of data that has some connection or was collected at the same time.

Tollgate: A structured review meeting used to ensure a project has completed a specific set of deliverables.

Unstable: A process that is unpredictable over time, usually due to special cause variation.

Value Add (VA): A process step that directly increases the value of a product or service, from the customers perspective.

Voice of the Customer (VOC): A Six Sigma phrase that refers to the range of results that are acceptable to a customer, whether in the form of a numeric specification or verbal feedback.

Voice of the Process (VOP): A Six Sigma phrase that refers to the range of results that are produced by a process.

'Z': The distance (in standard deviations) between the process average and the upper specification limit.

Index of Tools and Techniques

Index of Tools and Techniques

Index of Tools and Techniques